Strength of a Woman

Forgotten Heroines of the Bible

D0094358

AMY LeBLANC

 CIRCLE PRESS

Published by Circle Press, a division of Circle Media, Inc.

CIP Data is on file with the Library of Congress

ISBN 978-1-933271-24-8

PRINTED IN THE UNITED STATES OF AMERICA

8 7 6 5 4 3 2 1

FIRST EDITION

For Paula Ervin

A grandma whose strength was her faith and her family

Table of Contents

Introduction vii

Hannah 1

Judith 11

Queen Esther 45

Susanna 69

The Syropheonician Woman 87

The Widow of Nain 93

The Sinful Woman 101

The Hemorrhage Woman 119

The Samaritan Woman 129

Mary Magdalene 137

Mary's Memory 141

Introduction

"For when I am weak, then I am strong."

II COR 12:10

Everyone has had the experience of feeling weak. Physically, emotionally, spiritually, psychologically, mentally – the human experience of feeling tired and in need of rest is universal. Sometimes though, rest cannot be had. Responsibilities and duties demand us to push beyond what we think we are capable of. In those moments, strength is needed. People, then, are not strong because of the great things they do, but because of the small things they do even when they feel weak.

This book is not a theological or philosophical treatment of where women of the Bible found their strength. Nothing I propose in these pages is intended to serve as doctrinal teachings. I only highlight biblical examples to bring out the values of women. I try to allow them to tell their own stories, with a little creative interpretation and prayerful insight. By shining the light on eleven different women from the Old and New Testaments, I hope that other women will discover examples of strength.

The women I chose were real women like every other woman who ever lived and breathed. Like us all, they were women with weaknesses – they suffered, sinned, made bad choices, and even hurt others. At times they wavered in the seas of doubt, mistrust, and loneliness. But at other times they allowed their strength to shine. In spite of their failings, they came out of themselves to show love to another, to lend a hand, or even to save the day. They overcame their fears and misgivings in order to believe in God's love and grace. Even though they were weak, we look to them as examples of strength because of the fact that they turned to God in their weakness. They turned to God and, by reaching out to touch him in faith, they received the strength to love.

Jesus Christ is the real protagonist of these stories. He is the root of strength. He was the first to choose woman to play the most important role in the plan of salvation. He was the first to acknowledge woman as someone greater in times when she was considered property. He was the first to raise her when she had fallen. Jesus Christ gave woman a new identity, revealed her inner dignity, and treated her with respect even when she seemed not to deserve it. This is the Christ I hope each reader finds. The story of each woman's encounter with him is the story of your own encounter with him.

It is hoped that in reading these stories, one may find reasons to pray, the courage to hope, the strength to believe, and the will to love. For when we feel weak, then we need strength, and what better place to find it than faith in and love for God?

The Old Testament

Hannah

"Think of the Lord in goodness, and seek him in integrity of heart; because he is found by those who test him not, and he manifests himself to those who do not disbelieve him."
WISDOM OF SOLOMON 1:1-2

Eli entered the temple early that morning to offer his sacrifice of flour and ephah. He entered the cool, dimly lit chamber with a torch that cast an oval glow before him. In the rim of the light, he spotted two feet. He moved forward, holding the torch higher to find the long thin body of a woman lying prostrate on the marble floor, her forehead pressed to the ground and her lips moving silently. From under her veil, light strands of hair lay about in straggled heaps.

"Ach," thought Eli, *"another drunk got in during the night. When will it stop? This is a holy place; don't they know? Now we will have to begin another day with the purification rite."*

The woman hadn't yet noticed that the priest was standing over her. He called to her, "Woman, get up! You are profaning a holy place in your state of drunkenness. Have you no respect for God?"

She made no reply. Eli leaned forward to speak into her ear.

1

When he bent down, he listened to what she was mumbling. "Oh Lord of Hosts, if you will indeed look on the affliction of your maidservant, and remember me, and not forget me, but if you will give to your maidservant a son, then I will give him to the Lord all the days of his life, and no razor shall touch his head."

Eli straightened up. He had never heard a woman pray so fervently, however, as she began to shake in quiet sobs, Eli decided her piety's authenticity needed to be tested. *"I have been fooled too many times by these drunken women…"* he thought.

"Woman!" Eli put his foot under her rib and lifted it until she was sprawled over on her back. Crying out, she scrambled into a sitting position, crouching on the floor like a wounded animal, cheeks streaming with tears and arms hugging her legs to herself. Eli continued, "How long will you be drunken? Put away your wine from you."

At the accusation, Hannah flung herself prostrate before Eli, crying out, "No, my lord, I am a woman sorely troubled; do not regard your maidservant as a base woman, for all along I have been speaking out of my great anxiety and vexation." She grappled at his feet, trying to convince him.

Eli began to regret the roughness he had shown toward her. She was a pitiful sight. Bending down, he touched her head and she looked up at him, pulling herself up to sit. He stayed squatting next to her, listening.

"I have drunk neither wine nor strong drink, but I have been pouring out my soul to the Lord." A fresh well of tears gushed forward.

Eli put his hand upon her head in blessing, "Go in peace, and may the God of Israel grant your petition you have made to him."

The woman's face cleared. She looked with wonder at this

priest who was assuring her of Yahweh's providence. The God of Israel grant your petition… Hannah reflected on Eli's words. She got up, straightened her hair and tunic, and left the temple area. She reached the door but went running back to Eli, who was still watching her. Bowing her head, she said, "Let your maidservant find favor in your eyes." Eli looked into her face, now shining with glimmers of hope and anticipation. He nodded. Hannah reached down to grab her draping tunic and hurried out into the morning glow.

☙

"Hannah, there is something different about you. Last summer you had nothing but fits of sobbing and despair. You weren't even eating. Then after our trip to Shiloh, everything changed. And now you can't stop smiling." As Elkanah stopped to look at his favorite wife, she kept looking out the curtain of the litter they shared, smiling to herself. At his words, she turned to him and covered her smile with her hands. "Elkanah, the Lord has heard my prayer."

"Which prayer, Hannah?" She looked over to him. He studied her face, which was giving nothing away. Hannah watched his mind work it out. Nodding to confirm his thoughts, he stated, "I believe that your piety is the source of your joy."

"Yes, that, but also much more." She turned her head and laughed. "Elkanah, ask me again."

Elkanah's face clouded in confusion. "What? What games do you play with me?" His wife only smiled wider. "Just ask me why I am changed!" Elkanah decided to play along, as there was no other way of getting her to tell him. "Okay, why do you smile?"

She leaned forward and grabbed his hand. "Elkanah, what

have you wanted from me more than anything else?" Her husband pulled his hand away. "What? Now another question and you haven't even answered the one you made me ask. Enough games; I am impatient. Tell me now."

Hannah's eyes brimmed with joy. "Elkanah, we are to have a child!"

❧

"Elkanah, hold on there." Boeth put his hand on his friend's shoulder. Elkanah shook himself from his memories and looked at him. He said, "I am so afraid she will die. I was just remembering when she told me she was to have a child. You can't imagine our joy. And now, she has been laboring for a day and a half. I think it might have been better with just us two…"

"Don't say that. Just wait; she'll be fine. And when you hold your child in your arms, this fear will disappear forever and pass like a bad dream." Just then a great silence came from the adjacent room. Elkanah ran over to the curtain that covered the door. Just as he raised his hand to tear it away, a child's cry pierced through the silence.

"A son! Elkanah, it is a boy!" The midwife came running out. "You are the father of a healthy little boy!" Grabbing the maid, Elkanah questioned, "And Hannah? How is my wife?" The maid looked appalled that he could think anything could be wrong with her. "Why, she is asleep now. Resting. She will need lots of it too. It was a long labor, but she fought for that baby like no one I've ever seen." The midwife pulled herself away from Elkanah and disappeared behind the curtain.

Elkanah sat down on the chair in the hallway of his home, putting his head in his hands. He had never been more afraid of losing his beloved wife to the hands of death. For the first time in his life, Elkanah felt tears on his face. He looked up to heaven and whispered, "Praised be Yahweh."

Four days later, Elkanah stood over his wife's bed, staring down at the bundle of life in her arms. His hair was dark like his, but he had his mother's nose. "Hannah, what are we to name him?"

"He will be called Samuel, for I have asked him of the Lord." She smiled into his sleeping face. "Samuel will be his name then." Elkanah moved to the chair next to her bed to better see his wife. "I am already planning our trip to the temple to offer our yearly sacrifice. That is in a few months' time." Hannah looked up, frowning. "What's wrong?"

Her eyes began to fill with tears as she looked upon Samuel. "I have promised him to the Lord. He was a gift to me, and now I must give him back the next time I go up for the sacrifice." She looked at her husband. "How can I give him up so soon after I received him?"

Elkanah reached forward to touch his baby's soft head. "Hannah, at least you should wait until he is weaned. The priests can't have much to do with a child who needs a wet nurse. Let us keep Samuel for a few years before we give him back to the Lord."

With resignation, she replied, "Alright – as soon as the child is weaned, I will bring him, that he may appear in the presence of the Lord and abide there forever." She said this with tears in her eyes, but her face held the resolute courage that had emboldened her to petition Yahweh for a son in the first place. "Just wait, Hannah. Our sorrow will be great when we say goodbye to Samuel, but the Lord will repay us. He remembers his promises."

℥

Eli looked out from the door of the Lord's house, holding his weathered hand to shade his eyes from the setting sun's long fingered rays. On the horizon was a caravan of a good size. *"Another household come to offer the yearly sacrifice,"* he thought. He turned back to prepare the altar for offerings. He was still busy lighting the fire when he heard the people enter. A woman's voice rang through the great hall.

"Oh my lord! As you live, my lord!" Eli turned to see her coming toward him, a small boy following some feet behind, no more than three years old. "I am the woman who was standing here in your presence, praying to the Lord for this child." She turned and waved for her son to come forward. He came up and hid himself in her skirts, peeking out at the wrinkled old man who stared at him in wonder. The woman continued, "For this child I prayed and the Lord has granted me the petition I made to him. Therefore, as long as he lives, he is lent to the Lord."

Eli only stared at the dark-haired boy with bright brown eyes. The boy looked up at his mother with concern. She had sniffled. Eli saw she was fighting tears, refusing to look down at the boy tugging at her skirts. Behind her, servants were carrying in offerings of flour, wine, and a bull.

"Mama," his little voice whispered through the temple. "Mama, who is that man?"

Hannah couldn't ignore her son any longer; she bent down eye-level to speak to him. "That man is your friend now, Samuel. His name is Eli. He is going to teach you many things about the Lord." The boy reached up to play with the tassel of his mother's shawl. "But Mama, why are you crying?"

"Because I love you, Samuel, but I am not sad." She straightened up. The thought seemed to be like a light in her face when she said it. She began to speak as if to herself. "No, I'm not sad; my heart exults in the Lord, my strength is exalted in the Lord. My mouth derides my enemies, because I rejoice in your salvation." Hannah looked down at her son, who was looking at Eli skeptically. He didn't know what to make of the situation. Hannah took his hand and motioned to the servants. One of them brought the bull forward to be slaughtered on the altar. Little Samuel held his hands to his ears and closed his eyes tight to block out the noise and sight the bull made. Once the fire had caught, though, he watched the flames shoot up high into the air. The glow from the fire reflected on his face full of admiration for the sight.

His mother knelt down on the same cold spot she had pleaded for a son. Her prayer was different this time though. Her spirit was lifted as high as the smoke that now filled the temple ceiling. Again, she prayed aloud.

"There is none holy like the Lord, there is none besides him; there is no rock like our God. Talk no more so very proudly, let no arrogance come from your mouth, for the Lord is a God of knowledge, and by him actions are weighed. The bows of the mighty are broken, but the feeble gird on strength. Those who were full have hired themselves out for bread, but those who were hungry have ceased to hunger. The barren has borne seven."

At this Hannah looked down to Samuel, who was oblivious to his mother's prayer of thanksgiving, still fascinated by the fire. "But she who has many children is forlorn," she whispered. Eli moved closer and continued to listen to her prayer. "The Lord kills and brings to life; he brings down to Sheol and raises it up. The Lord makes poor and makes rich. He brings low; he also exalts. He raises up the poor from the dust; he lifts the needy from the ash heap to make them sit with princes and inherit the seat of honor. For the pillars of the earth are the Lord's, and on them he has set the world." Hannah broke from her contemplation and became aware of Eli staring at her. She gazed back at him, then down at Samuel, who had fallen asleep at her knees. Again she began to pray as she meditated on her son's delicate features, the way his nose was shaped, the curl of his long eyelashes as they rested on his round cheeks. He was so small, so defenseless. She feared for him. "He will guard the feet of his faithful ones, and the wicked will be cut off by darkness; for not by might shall a man prevail…" Hannah's words faded away and she continued to contemplate her little boy. Eli stared at the two of them, awestruck.

"Woman, how can you find the courage to return your only son to the Lord?" Instead of turning to Eli to answer him, Hannah continued to gaze at Samuel. "Because, my lord, Samuel was a gift given freely to me. I never deserved to have him. It was through no merit of my own but only by the Lord's mercy and goodness that I was granted a son. And now I can thank Yahweh by giving him that which is most precious to me. Samuel was given to me freely, and freely I give him to serve the Lord all the days of his life." At these words Hannah stood and picked the boy up into her arms. "I am young still and can still give many things to the Lord. And when I am old, I will have the consolation of knowing that my own child belongs to him and continues to give to him on my behalf." She kissed her son's soft cheeks and forehead, and then surrendered him to the priest's arms. Eli held the child awkwardly; one of Samuel's arms hung limply at an odd angle. Hannah placed it neatly over his little belly. She brushed his head and looked at Eli. He said, "May the Lord grant you blessings for all you've given him." She nodded, brushed the tears from her face, and left the temple.

The sun blinded her eyes as they adjusted from the darkness she came from. Elkanah approached. He stood before her in an anguished silence. "Are you ready to go home?" His voice broke, but he didn't give in to tears. Instead, he watched as she nodded with tears streaming down her own face. Taking her by the hand, he put his arm around her and helped her into the litter, walking alongside it as the household made its way back to Ephraim. After a long distance, in which all traveled in sad silence, the servants listened as the two began to converse about what blessings the Lord might yet bestow. Yet none could fathom all the great things that would be done thanks to their generosity, for Samuel would one day prove to be a great prophet for all of Israel.

Judith

"I bless the Lord who counsels me; even at night my heart exhorts me. I keep the Lord always before me; with the Lord at my right, I shall never be shaken. Therefore my heart is glad, my soul rejoices; my body also dwells secure. For you will not abandon me to death, nor let your faithful servant know corruption. You will show me the path to life, abounding joy in your presence, delights at your right hand forever."

PSALM 16:7-11

Crickets hummed incessantly in the warm night. Their music pierced through the smoky tent. It was warmer than usual for summer, but then again Ecbatana wasn't Nineveh. No one was accustomed to such temperatures down there. Even Nebuchadnezzar's guards were uncomfortable in the heat, but they wouldn't dare abandon post while the king was awake. They stood watch – or rather, watching – as silhouettes passed back and forth on the gray tent wall. Low murmurs and an occasional shout reached out into the peaceful night.

However, the scene inside wasn't as peaceful. Tension hung above the map unrolled across the rough wooden table. The air was heavy with smoke from the torches and summer humidity, although the sun had long gone. Eight men leaned over the table, talking gruffly, eyebrows knit and foreheads wrinkled, all donned with shaggy beards. All but one. His was trimmed and daintily curled. He had a wig that caused him to perspire more than the others. He was speaking loudest.

"No! We will not suffer any further disgraces! It has been eighteen years since those fleas from the West refused to help, and now that we have defeated King Arphaxad, we can turn the revenge upon them that I swore by my sword." The man speaking paused to let his words sink in, challenging the others present with his gaze. "Tomorrow, sound the camp and announce we are leaving for Nineveh." Even when he was upset, it was hard not to laugh at Nebuchadnezzar. He frowned, trying to look fierce, but his rosebud mouth looked dainty. His soft, fleshy-pink cheeks were like puffed-up cherries peeking out from above his beard.

"My lord, why back to Nineveh?" a decrepit adviser spoke up.

"Because, I have a new law to pass in my kingdom." He looked around at his advisers' puzzled faces. Heaving a loud sigh, exasperated with having to explain himself to everyone, he began "I am now going to be known as the great King Nebuchadnezzar, lord of the whole earth! And I want the whole earth to know it, so they can worship me. That will teach those Westerners a lesson!" His exasperation turned into a menacing air.

One adviser, even older than the other, cleared his throat. "My lord, may I ask?" Nebuchadnezzar snapped at Brugesh. "What is it? Don't try and talk me down. My mind is set and I will follow through with my word." The rosebud frown came close to looking fierce.

Bowing deeply, Brugesh redressed himself, "Yes, my lord, I believe the opportunity is ripe and we should go forward with your plans. I only ask, who will head the army? Surely it must be someone who can withstand the western climates and people. It is a different world from ours."

The king rolled his eyes and spoke in condescending tones. "Brugesh, I am well aware of the extent of the task, and I know what I am doing, which is why I have chosen Holofernes to carry it to completion." At the name of his most prized general, Nebuchadnezzar's stance once again challenged his advisors to contest. A respectful and awe-filled hush fell over them. It was well known that Holofernes was an excellent general, second only to Nebuchadnezzar. Holofernes was ruthless. He didn't have the heart to spare even an infant if it was of the enemy.

Nebuchadnezzar seemed pleased by the silence of his men. "Tomorrow by noon, we leave for Nineveh." He pushed over the crystal that held down an end of the map. It snapped back into a scroll. Servants came to clear the table, and the men all left for their tents.

☙

"Holofernes, arise." The great king motioned servants to raise Holofernes, who had prostrated himself to his king upon entering the hall. They scurried across the green marble floor that had been imported from the Far East. Stone columns sustained the ceiling that soared high above the men. In the center was a pond filled with lilies and fish. Couches, tapestries, and plants were scattered about at odd intervals, each with a different view. It was cool in the hall. Wind blew from the north and brought the scent of flowers. Different-colored birds swooped in and out, calling to one another.

"My lord and great king, I am here to serve you." Holofernes kept his head slightly inclined to show his respect.

"Come, good friend, sit and eat with me." He glanced up and saw Nebuchadnezzar reclining on a couch, eating figs. Behind him on the back wall was a tapestry as high as the ceiling. It portrayed a battle the king had won many years before. Holofernes noticed the king's stout torso had been flattered in the picture. His gut was at least two times trimmer than what reality offered.

"Are you admiring my accomplishments? It was a victory worth more than words can tell. Yet, even a depiction falls short. It doesn't capture the smell of the men and blood or the feel of the armor and horse." Holofernes stopped studying the tapestry to look at the king, who was lost in a memory. Holofernes cleared his throat. Nebuchadnezzar stood up, toppling the bowl of fruit and pushing away the little boy who was holding a fan twice his size. "Holofernes, you are my greatest general, second only to me." He approached him and braced his shoulders, looking him straight in the eyes. Holofernes nodded at the attempted compliment.

"I have a new task for you." The king cut to the point. "This task, if you fulfill it as I expect you to, will make you greater than five tapestries can tell." Nebuchadnezzar turned again to look at his wall and continued to speak. "It is a great undertaking, which is why I entrust it to you." He paused and turned to see what his man would say.

Holofernes showed no sign of eagerness, only the cool readiness of a well-trained soldier. "Where to, my lord?" This response earned him a slap on the back from the king. "To the West, my friend."

Holofernes nodded. Pulling him by the arm, they began to walk the length of the pool. The king continued, "It is a chance for revenge that only you know how long I have waited for. Every city, every town that refused to assist me in my time of need will now be calling upon me to assist them when I come down on them like a night of death. Then they will turn to me when their gods won't even save them. Then I will be their god. Then I will be king of all this earth. And you, Holofernes, will be at my side."

Holofernes stopped and fell to one knee. "I am at your disposal; tell me and I will act." Nebuchadnezzar smiled; he knew he would have the help he needed. "Thus says the great king, the lord of the whole earth." He raised his voice so his scribes could hear. The bald-headed men sitting cross-legged on the floor began to scribble furiously upon their tablets. "When you leave my presence, take with you men confident in their strength to the number of one hundred and twenty thousand for soldiers and twelve thousand cavalry. Go and attack the whole West Country, because they disobeyed my orders."

Nebuchadnezzar had been pacing as he spoke. He stopped in front of a delicate flower that protruded from a tree and was obstructing his path. Plucking the flower, he twirled it between his fingers as he continued. "Tell them to prepare earth and water, for I am coming against them in my anger and will cover the whole face of the earth with the feet of my armies." His voice began to grow harsh with hatred. The flower's little stem had gone limp. Nebuchadnezzar began to pluck the petals with each emphatic sentence he voiced. "I will hand them over to be plundered by my troops till their wounded shall fill the valley; every brook and river will be filled with their dead and overflow. And I will lead them away captive to the ends of the earth. You will go and seize all their territory for me in advance. They will yield themselves to you, and you will hold them for me till the day of their punishment."

The king threw down what was left of the flower and was now shouting at Holofernes. He came close to him again and spoke straight to him, softer – *dangerously* soft. "But if they refuse, your eye will not spare them and you will hand them over to slaughter and plunder throughout your whole region. For as I live and by the power of my kingdom, what I have spoken, my hand will execute. And you, take care not to trespass any of your sovereign's commands."

At that, King Nebuchadnezzar dismissed Holofernes. He stamped his foot twice on the floor and servants came rushing in to clear away the fruit and assist their king. The general bowed his way out of the hall.

Throughout the next week, Holofernes called together troops and provisions; the king supplied them with a huge amount of gold and silver, enough to fill a sea. And after a week they marched west to cover the whole face of the earth with chariots and horsemen, to prepare the way for the king.

☙

Three weeks into the campaign, the air was thick with the dust from fleeing people and the smoke of burning buildings. The blood of the enemies drenched the meadows and fields. Holofernes descended upon one town after another, bringing with him death and destruction. Cries of fear and moans of sorrow rang throughout nights lit by trails of fire. He marched across the plains of Bectileth, bringing every town to its knees by force, until they reached the Euphrates and Mesopotamia.

"All the land Holofernes is stepping foot on is submitting to his crushing hands. People are giving up their gods and towns to preserve their lives and families." The man on the corner of the street jumped onto an overturned crate to be heard by the crowd that was gathering around him. In Israel, it was easy to gather a crowd over a bit of news. Nieko was from Greece and had brought his poetic talents to Israel, where he adopted its language and used it for his benefit. Times like these meant promising returns from some synagogue officials, who paid him to bring people to pray and offer sacrifice. "People of Israel," he called out with a hint of dramatic anguish, "destruction is creeping ever closer to your homes. Temples are being leveled and whole races are being taken captive. Captive! That is sadly a familiar word to us all." The crowd doubled in size as murmurs of fright rippled through. Nieko was in his glory.

"How well we know what it means to be captive! How sore our memories still are! At last we have been enjoying some semblance of normality and peace after so many years of war and unrest. Yet, just when we think we are being blessed by God, another enemy rises up. Holofernes comes in the name of Nebuchadnezzar, demanding everyone to submit to calling him king and god of the universe!" A distraught woman cried out, "What are we to do?" At the back of the crowd, a prominent figure advanced toward the center. "Israelites!" The crowd grew silent at the voice of their high priest, Reuben. "I was walking through the streets only to come upon this gossip corner to find unrest and disturbance." He moved to the center and spoke. "What Nieko says is true, but we will not allow our trust in Yahweh to fail." Nieko scowled at Reuben and slipped out of sight. Reuben let him go.

Turning back to the crowd, he said, "Already I have summoned every district from Samaria, Jericho, and the valley of Salem to come together and seize the high hilltops surrounding our country. Providence has seen to it that our harvests are already in and secure, so we will be able to fortify ourselves with provisions enough for war. I have written to the cities facing the east, the passageway that Holofernes will take. I ordered them to fortify their cities so that Judea would be protected." By this time, the crowd was calm and quiet, thanking Reuben and Yahweh for the work already done. Little by little, they began to break up, wandering in different directions to spread the word that Israel was taking actions of defense.

The sun sank from her high position in the sky, and the talk continued around firesides and supper tables. As the food disappeared and the fires dimmed, the men and women ceased their thoughts of war and captivity for the night, surrendering to the bliss of sleep.

As the waxing moon rose and night settled in, one of Israel's towns to the east, Bethulia, could not sleep. Every person from the wisest elder to the smallest child put on sackcloth and ashes. Men and women walked about with faces gaunt from fasting. There was a constant murmur of wailing and pleading to the Lord. The streets near the synagogue smelled of incense and offerings. Their cries of supplication were many and sincere. Bethulia didn't want any more widows clothed in black or orphaned children filling their street corners. The whole people cried out to their God, confident that he would not forget them. Reuben reassured them that the Lord who had given them a king and had rescued them from captivity would surely send help.

☙

"General, there is news of Israel." Holofernes looked up from the map he was studying to see his messenger standing before him.

"What is it?" he barked.

The messenger began to look as though he would rather not be the bearer of the news he had. "Sir, the land of Israel has fortified its hilltops and barricaded its plains. The people are preparing for war."

"What?" Holofernes roared. He stood up and knocked over the table he was sitting at, catapulting its contents across the tent. The veins in his neck began to bulge and red splotches appeared. The messenger was slowly backing out of the tent. "Stop!" shouted the general. He froze. "I want you to get every one of my advisers in here now! Bring in the counselors and princes of Moab and the commanders of Ammon. I want all the governors of the coastland here now!" The messenger skittered out of the tent and took off at a run for his horse.

Holofernes was still pacing his tent when, an hour later, the advisers and governors began to arrive. They came in to greet him, but their jovial spirits evaporated as soon as they saw his stern countenance. They stood in awkward silence, casting quick glances at one another.

At last Holofernes stopped pacing. He faced the men and, cutting any cordiality, began to speak. "Tell me of the Israelites. Who are these people who live in the hill country? What are their strengths? What are their weaknesses? And who rules them that, of all those in the west, they have refused to come out and meet me?" By this time he was shouting and slamming his fist on the table his servant had righted. His neck was splotching red again. The governors began to look from one to the other, trying to motion with their eyes to get another to answer besides himself. Holofernes continued to breathe heavily through his thick nose until one man stepped forward. His name was Achior, and he was the leader of the Ammonites. His bald head was shiny, and his eyes were uncommonly light. His face was serene, but his quivering tunic betrayed his fright.

"My lord, let your servant speak to you of the peoples of the hill country." Holofernes nodded curtly.

"They are a people with a long history, descended from the Chaldeans, for they used to inhabit the land of Mesopotamia until their god – for they are unique in that they have but one god they worship – he called them out of that land of many gods.

They came to Egypt. There they prospered and multiplied until the king became jealous of their number. He enslaved them. For hundreds of years they lived thus until a man came in the name of their one god and freed them. He did this by bringing famines and plagues upon all of Egypt. Their god is powerful. He dried up the Red Sea for them to cross. He led them through the desert of Sinai for forty years and returned them safely to the hill country over the Jordan, where they now live. He gave them power to drive out all those who inhabited that land. That is how they settled that wilderness. As long as they do not offend their god, they prosper. But as soon as they sin against him, he looses his wrath upon them. Theirs is a god who hates iniquity. By their sins they have paid fully through battles lost, captivity and a destroyed temple. Now they are returned though. Their sanctuary is in Jerusalem where they are ruled by their high priest."

Achior paused to see what Holofernes thought. He was met only with a cold stare, so he took another breath and continued. "So, my lord, their god is their strength as long as they are in his grace. But when they turn from him, they are sure to meet destruction. I advise that we seek out if they are in transgression, and this will secure our victory. However, if we find them in no offense to their god, then we better pass them by, for their god will surely defend them and we will be put to shame before the whole world."

At once, the governors erupted into complaints. Their voices mounted as each tried to make his heard above the other. Holofernes continued to stare down Achior, who was now playing fretfully with his rings. The governors continued to shout. "Lord Holofernes, we will not be frightened by one god! We have many gods and King Nebuchadnezzar behind us. We must make war on this hill country and devour them with your vast army."

"Enough!" Holofernes rounded the table and approached Achior until they were face to face. Achior came only to Holfernes' broad shoulders; he had to look up into his raging face to see his eyes. Holofernes spoke quietly, restraining the anger inside that seeped out through his eyes and snarling mouth. "And who are you Achior to tell me when and when not to make war? And who are you to say the Israelite's god will protect them when we come in the name of the god Nebuchadnezzar? Who is god except he?"

The governors watched as Achior seemed to shrink under the powerful presence of their general. "Nebuchadnezzar has sent me and I will be victorious in his name. My army will come as one man and crush that hill country! We will burn them up, and their mountains will be steeped with their blood and their fields will be strewn with their dead. They cannot withstand us! They will utterly perish. So has King Nebuchadnezzar spoken and so will it be that none of his words will be spoken in vain!" Holofernes was brimming with rage. He towered over Achior and spat in his face as he thundered. Achior shrank still more, but it was too late to attempt dissuading Holofernes' fury.

"Achior, you worm," snarled the great general. "You will pay for your arrogance." Holofernes turned to his servant. "Bagoas, today Achior has found his lot. Take him and hand him over to the men of Israel." Holofernes looked at the other governors, all cowering where they stood. "Tomorrow we move camp to the valley of Bethulia. If you stand with me, your reward will be great. If not, you may return to your homes, but with the knowledge that I will eventually come to you and crush you and your household while you sleep." Each governor in turn pledged his loyalty and quickly left. Holofernes didn't even look at Achior as he was led out of the tent, bound hand and foot.

☙

The open heavens were shining with white stars and a sliver of moon. Only the chink-chink of Achior's chains and the tramping of feet broke the stillness of the night. He and two slaves trudged through the hills near Bethulia in silence. Every movement was painful. The ropes had been tied so roughly that they cut into his wrists, and his feet were aching from dragging such heavy chains.

Suddenly, a whistle was heard. Achior ducked as the arrow pierced the slave next to him in the arm. It seemed to be a sign for the slaves, because they both took off, leaving their charge. Two more men soon appeared and closed in on Achior. They were dressed in dark turbans, but he could see their eyes reflecting the stars. He opened his mouth to tell them who he was but was knocked over the head before a sound escaped. He slumped to the ground as the stars faded from his sight.

The men of Bethulia carried their prisoner to the city. The next morning he was unbound and brought before the magistrates. There, they placed Achior in their midst. His head was still spinning from his unwelcome sleep. As he sat down before the crowd of men, he looked around. Fifteen men in somber clothing watched him from beneath heavy head-coverings. Their eyes where darker than the men Achior knew. Yet even though their color was different, he could see there was no malice. He realized he was not up for trial but was there to prove his friendship. Sitting back, he recounted his tale to them. He held nothing back, sharing all that Holofernes was plotting. When he finished, the eldest stood up and shouted out, "Lord God of heaven, we thank you for delivering this man to us. Now we can protect your people consecrated to you, and the enemy can perish in their arrogance."

At that moment, however, a man came running in, shouting and rolling his eyes like that of a terrified horse. "God save us! We are all to perish in this city! The warriors from the east have encamped in our valley! They have seized our water supply! We will die of famine if not of thirst! God save us!"

Uzziah, the chief magistrate, stood up and brought order back to the counsel. "Men, command every person and animal in the city to fast and put on sackcloth and ashes. Pray to the Lord our God to spare us from our enemy." Three heralds rushed out to proclaim this at every street corner.

Achior watched as day after day crept by. The summer sun continued to beat down upon man and animal, oblivious to their cracked lips and parched throats. Thirty-four days passed in which the water was rationed. Like flowers removed from the vine, the people of Bethulia began to wilt. Women and children were fainting in the streets, weeping dry sobs of suffering. They were left without strength, and so they complained to Uzziah and their God.

Uzziah did what he could to console them, but he had nothing to rely on except for God's intercession. He needed a miracle or he would be forced to submit to the Assyrians.

☙

"Ulyssa, I need you to send a message." The sturdy slave girl came to stand by her mistress, ready to take the scroll. Judith sat down and began to write, mumbling to herself as the words flowed from her stylus. Ulyssa watched her mistress' hand move across the scroll and recalled when she had arrived four years earlier, after Judith's husband had died. She remembered coming into that house and helping her mistress move from her luxurious house to a tent on the roof. Judith never wore her fine clothing or sparkling jewels after that. For four years the routine had been the same. Every morning, Ulyssa prepared a simple meal and took it up to the roof. Judith would come out of the tent, having been up since dawn praying. The two would eat together in silence, and Judith would go to prepare for the day. She would always dress in her ugly widow's garb, but even that didn't hide her fresh beauty. All these thoughts streamed through her mind as she watched her mistress write. Putting the stylus down and closing the jar of ink, Judith turned to Ulyssa. "You can take this directly to Uzziah." She handed the sealed scroll to her and continued speaking to herself as she often did. "Maybe this will help him see that the Lord will not abandon us." Judith's voice faded off, and she drifted out of the room to go to her midday prayer.

Ulyssa grabbed the bright blue tunic her mistress had given her as a gift. She deftly wrapped her head and tucked the scroll inside it. Flinging the door open she leapt out, running smack into a man's thick chest.

"What is this all about?" his gruff voice shouted above her. Ulyssa stumbled backward and pulled her tunic, which was tangled from the collision, off her face. When she could at last see, she looked up right at Uzziah. "Woman, what are you doing running about without looking where you are going?"

"Forgive me, my lord." The poor girl fell into a half bow to hide her red face. Uzziah, obviously impatient, spoke again. "Well, are you going to let me pass? I am here to see your mistress."

Ulyssa looked up, surprised. "My lord, I have a scroll here that I was to bring to you. I didn't know you were at the door. It is from my mistress."

Uzziah studied the somewhat crumpled scroll. He snatched

it from her and broke the seal. He read two lines and looked up at Ulyssa, who was waiting with downcast eyes. "Okay, can you show me to your mistress?" Ulyssa nodded and opened the door. She led him into a room to wait and went to her mistress.

Judith looked up from her prayer at the footsteps of her servant. "What is it, Ulyssa? Returned so soon? What of the message I sent you with?"

"The magistrate Uzziah is waiting for you in a room downstairs. He was at the door when I went to leave. He is here to see you." Judith's eyebrows rose. "The Lord surely has brought him so I can convince him myself." She stood and began to make her way down to the main house. Ulyssa meekly followed behind.

Uzziah was standing when the women entered the room. He moved forward to greet Judith, but she cut him off. "Listen to me, ruler of the people of Bethulia! You have come to seek my advice, and I give it before you ask." Uzziah's smile fell from his face as his eyes widened in surprise. "What you have decided is not right! Never promise to surrender this city to the Assyrians. Do you not believe in the power of our God? You have put him to the test to deliver us under pain of our fidelity!" Judith stopped to make sure that Uzziah was listening to her. He was staring at her with a slightly opened mouth, unable to answer such powerful words from a woman. She continued, "You have put the Almighty to the test, but you will never know anything. You cannot plumb the depths of the human heart, nor find out what a man is thinking; how do you expect to search out God, or find out his thoughts, or comprehend his ways?" Judith's voice softened on these words. Uzziah seemed to lose some of the fire he had come with.

Judith looked at him with pleading eyes. "Uzziah, we cannot afford to provoke the Lord our God's anger. We must trust and give thanks to him that he has deemed us as worthy as our forefathers to put us to this test, just as he tested their faith." Uzziah sat down on the couch at his side. He put his head in his hands with a defeated sigh. "Judith, but what am I to do? The people of Bethulia are disheartened by their thirst. They are demanding that we take action." He looked up at her, ready to continue but again she cut him off. "To take action is precisely what I am proposing to do. But I am suggesting that we take action on the Lord's side, not against him."

Uzziah stood up and faced Judith. "What are you suggesting?"

Judith closed her eyes and leaned back on the couch. "What I am about to do will be told through generations to come." Straightening up, she opened her eyes and looked at Uzziah. "Stand at the city gate tonight, and I will go out with my maid; within five days the Lord will deliver Israel by my hand. I only ask that you do not try to find out my plan, for I cannot tell you until it is completed."

Uzziah frowned at her as he considered her words. After some minutes he nodded. "Alright, go in peace, and may the Lord God go before you to take revenge upon our enemies." Ulyssa hadn't left the room during the entire discussion, and she watched Uzziah as he gave his blessing. She wondered if he really meant it or was only seizing the last resort he had. She led him out the room to the front door. Upon returning, she found her mistress still standing where she had left her. When Ulyssa entered the room, Judith went into action.

"Ulyssa, I am going to offer incense to the Lord this evening. When I return, have a bath prepared for me. Bring out the garments and jewelry and oils I wore when my husband lived. Bring out my comb and tiara, my gayest apparel, my sandals and bracelets and anklets. Prepare a basket of fruits, grain, and wine enough for five days. Prepare yourself as well, for you must accompany me in this trial."

Ulyssa nodded and watched Judith retire to her tent to pray and offer incense. The faithful servant stood for a few moments where she was. She heard Judith's footsteps ascend the stairs and then disappear onto the roof. She looked about her at the same house and rooms she knew so well. Yet today, they looked different. Now there was an air of mystery and anticipation that hung in the air as particles of dust do in the sunlight. Ulyssa realized she was musing and set to work. She pulled Judith's fine clothes out of trunks covered in dust and happy memories. Her old room was soon filled with brilliant colors that echoed with the voices of gatherings and festivals of days past.

When the basket brimming with food and wine was prepared and the bath was drawn, Judith descended the stairs. Ulyssa gasped at her changed appearance. Gone were the ashes and sackcloth. Judith was in a white robe, her hair was down, and her face was shining like that of a messenger from heaven. Her face remained serene as she prepared. Ulyssa had never seen her mistress in such a state of peace and silent determination. She dressed with as much care as if she were going to greet the king of Israel. Judith pulled a green, glittering tunic from her wardrobe. This she put over her white robe and added layer after layer of gold jewelry studded with diamonds and sapphires. Ulyssa combed her hair until it shone and helped her with her many jewels. She swept her hair up and secured it with a silver comb, then helped her arrange a veil the same color as her tunic. From head to foot, she shone like a rare flower in the sun. On her feet were sandals made of leather with small precious stones embroidered into the lacing. When she walked, her clothing softly rustled, and her anklets and bracelets jingled. The end effect was breathtaking. Judith was beautiful in her widow's garb and ashes, but in all her finery she was stunning.

"Aren't you afraid?" Judith gave an understanding smile to her beloved maid. "I was, but in my prayer, I entrusted myself to the Lord. And now, I believe he will act, for our power lies not in us, but in him. The Assyrians surround us on every side, and he will strike down the slave with his prince and the prince with his servant; he will crush their arrogance by the hand of a woman. He is not the God of the mighty but the Almighty God of the lowly. And we are his lowly servants, here to do his will. That is why I do not fear."

❦

Dusk had fallen upon Bethulia when Judith and her maid stole away from their house and met the magistrate at the city gate. Ulyssa noticed the way his eyebrows shot up when he recognized Judith. His frank admiration of her beauty was evident. Uzziah blessed her again and opened the gate for her.

She and her maid hurried out. The men guarding the gate, along with the magistrate of the city, watched them pass through the valley until they could no longer see them.

❦

"Noël, wake up! There is someone in the camp from the city. They are bringing her to Holofernes' tent now!"

"Her? You mean they captured a woman?"

The foot soldier scowled at his tentmate. "No, fool! She escaped from her city and surrendered to us. She came this night and has asked to speak to the general to give him advice on how to attack her people."

Noël's attention was caught. He jumped up from his mat and

28

flew from his tent toward the main part of the camp. He arrived
along with hundreds of other foot soldiers in time to see a troop
of at least one hundred escorting two women.

It was night, but many torches and cooking fires illuminated
the people. Great shouts and whistles erupted from the crowd
as the women passed. Noël craned his neck to get a good look.
What he saw made him understand the commotion. He recognized a woman with her maid. It is true that a soldier, living
among only men for months and years on end, will find any
woman attractive, but this was different. Never in his life had
he beheld a woman of such exotic beauty. There were no words
to express her features and grace of stance and character. All
too quickly the escort passed, and the soldiers dissolved into
small groups to discuss this woman. Noël drifted from group to
group, listening to their conversations. One group caught his
attention more than any other.

"Who can despise these people who have women like that
among them? We should be allying ourselves with them, not
destroying them!"

"No! Surely not a man of them had better be left alive, for if
we let them go, they will be able to ensnare the entire world!"

☙

Upon entering Holofernes' tent, Ulyssa forced herself not
to gasp at the luxury in which he lived. The general himself was
at a desk next to his bed. There was a glittering canopy above it,
woven with purple, gold, emeralds, and precious stones. It was
magnificent. When she and her mistress entered, he rose and
picked up the silver lantern next to him. He held it up to study
Judith and her maid. They both fell down to offer homage, but he

motioned for his slaves to raise them. When he saw her full in the face, he reacted much as Uzziah had at the city gate.

Holofernes spoke first. "Take courage, woman. Do not be afraid in your heart, for I will not hurt anyone who has chosen to serve Nebuchadnezzar as lord." He paused, and Judith nodded regally. Holofernes followed, "Tell me now, why have you fled from your people and come to my tent with your maid?" He glanced at Ulyssa at these words, and she lowered her eyes discreetly.

Judith began to speak. Her voice was full of confidence. "Allow me to speak, lord, that I may serve Nebuchadnezzar, the king of the entire world." Upon Holofernes' nod, she continued. "In my city, we have heard of your wisdom and skill. I know you are a good man, thoroughly informed and marvelous in military strategy. Some weeks ago, men captured a defector from your camp. Perhaps you know of Achior?" Holofernes' jaw tightened. "I see you remember him. Men brought him before our magistrates and he told of your plans to destroy our city if we do not come out to you. Our people were ready to hold out against your army and remain faithful to our Lord. But then you blocked off our water supply. My people proved to be weaker than they determined to be. Now they are preparing to offend our God by killing their bulls and using all that his laws forbid to eat. They have decided to eat the firstfruits of the grain, which is supposed to be consecrated and set aside for the temple priests. They have sent to Jerusalem and wait on the permission to return. When they get word, their day of iniquity will visit them, and they will be handed over to you to be destroyed.

"When I, your servant, heard of this, I fled to inform you. God has sent me to do things that will astonish the whole world and generations to come." She paused. Holofernes was listening with amused attention, smiling ironically. "I see you are attentive as to the happenings of my people." Holofernes nodded, crossing his arms. "Perhaps the rituals of my people baffle your practical soldier's mind?" Holofernes laughed at her accuracy in judging his reactions. Judith smiled knowingly and continued, "Yes, you are not used to our one God, but know that your servant before you is religious and listens to this God. He speaks to me, for I am faithful to him. For this reason, allow me to stay here with you. Each night, I will go out to the valley to pray and offer incense to my God. He will enlighten me on the day my people have betrayed him. On that day I will lead you around to a pass behind the mountains. I will lead you through toward Judea and then on to Jerusalem. There you will take power over them. Not so much as a dog will growl at you, for this has been revealed to me by my God."

Ulyssa was watching Holofernes intently during this prophecy. He listened carefully, keenly absorbed in Judith's words. When she explained how she would lead him to Jerusalem, he began to nod his head, massaging his chin. At last Judith finished and Holofernes called for his servant. "Bagoas! Come at once." Immediately he appeared from behind a flap that served as a wall. "Bagoas! God has done well to send us this woman who is not only beautiful in appearance but wise in speech as well. We will follow her plan." Holofernes watched Judith. She smiled politely and bowed her head in thanks. "Take her and her maid to where my fine silver is kept. Set a table and serve her from my food and wine." Judith stepped forward. "My lord, I have brought my own food and wine. I ask only for a place for my maid and me to sleep before we go out at night to pray." Holofernes seemed puzzled that she would not accept his food, but he shrugged at her strange custom and permitted her a tent.

After she had left, Bagoas waited for his master's command.

Holofernes was musing over all that had taken place, admiring his turn of luck. Finally he turned to his manservant. "Bagoas, let her and her maid go out and pray. When they return, invite the woman to my tent to eat with me. Her maid may accompany her if she wishes. Prepare a table and wine." Bagoas bowed himself out of Holofernes' presence.

∝

"And you aren't afraid now? Even after all those lies you told to that fearsome man?"

"Ulyssa, stop fretting and hold still. We are still under the Lord's protection. Now eat something for we are going out to pray in the valley."

"You mean you were serious about that?" she whispered fiercely, afraid someone might be listening through the thin tent wall.

"Of course I was. There is yet much to be done tonight, and it is only in prayer that we find the strength to follow God's will." Ulyssa's stomach clenched at the thought of where God's will would lead them that night. She barely managed to choke down some fruit and wine before leaving for the valley to pray.

Once away from the camp, Ulyssa's fear heightened at every sound and movement. The wind blew through the high grass, making it ripple like water in the moonlight. Judith found a clearing and spread out her mat. Ulyssa stood nearby, trying to pray, but was more occupied with keeping watch. After some time, Judith rose. "There, let us go now and meet the enemy. Dear Ulyssa, be ready to stay by me through everything. I need you to remain silent no matter what. Don't cry, girl; no harm will come to us. Trust in God." Ulyssa nodded through her tears and trudged back to camp with her mistress.

They made their way through the sleeping camp back to their tent. Ulyssa entered it first and gave a gasp. She wasn't expecting to find Bagoas standing in it. He smiled with sneering eyes. "My lord Holofernes has requested your presence to sup with him." Ulyssa gulped, but Judith consented as if she were expecting it.

If Ulyssa thought she couldn't feel any more fear, she was wrong, for it only doubled as she approached Holofernes' tent and heard the number of people there. It wasn't just supper they were having; it was a banquet. Judith entered the tent with assurance. Everyone there grew quiet at her presence. Holofernes broke through them and buoyantly shouted for everyone to continue drinking and being merry. The noise erupted again into cheers and laughter. Ulyssa almost fell over in shock as Judith laughed out loud and called her to prepare her some wine. Ulyssa took the wine she had brought and served a goblet for her. Holofernes, pleased at her response, took a long swig from the jar in his fist. The reddish liquid sloshed down his beard when he tried to grin while guzzling it. Ulyssa hid a face of disgust. She turned and went to the corner of the tent where a basket of kittens were watching the carousing. She sat next to them and scooped one into her lap. For the next hours she focused more on playing with the little thing rather than on the drunkenness around her.

Judith mingled among the people, the whole time with a glass of wine in her hand. Holofernes followed her around for the most part, distracted only often enough for Judith to dump the wine from her glass when his back was turned. Upon turning back, he would always offer her more wine. Every time someone offered a toast, which was quite often, she would hold the glass to her lips but wouldn't swallow. She swaggered around, giving loud shouts and laughing raucously at Holofernes' every antic. The hours lengthened and the wine continued to flow. The noise only grew. The shouts and songs mounted until at last, one by one, the guests began to pass out. When that happened, servants came in to drag their lifeless, slobbering bodies to their tents.

Finally, the last soldier slumped over in his chair. A servant dragged him out, leaving only Judith, Holofernes, and Ulyssa. Even Bagoas was nowhere to be seen. Ulyssa sat in her corner, watching to see what would happen next.

Bagoas entered, completely sober, and scoffed at the two drunks laughing hysterically. "My lord Holofernes, your room is ready." Holofernes teetered over to Bagoas and slapped him on the back. "Good, Baggs! Turn in for the night then." His words slurred as he spoke. "I'll see you tomorrow afternoon then; after all, it's almost morning, right?" He took another gulp of wine from the bottle that hadn't left his hand all night. "Right, to-morrow afternoon then." Bagoas pushed Holofernes and Judith toward the room and left the tent, closing it up for the night. He hadn't even noticed Ulyssa. She got up and followed behind Judith, who had gone into the room with Holofernes. A single silver torch dimly lighted the room, and Holofernes' jeweled canopy twinkled in the flickering flame.

When Ulyssa entered, Holofernes was standing at the foot of his elaborate bed, looking at Judith through bloodshot eyes. "Do you know?" he slurred, "you are so pretty that you remind me of, of…" he opened his mouth to speak, but instead a great belch came out. Judith backed away from him as he swayed like a great tree in a windstorm. As he fell, his head hit a wooden chest and smacked back at a painful angle. Judith looked down at his trunk of a body strewn across the floor. A gash on his forehead trickled blood. She looked up at Ulyssa through tears. For the first time, Ulyssa noticed the circles under her eyes and the creases on her forehead from exhaustion. She came to her side to support her. "We can go home now," she whispered.

Judith pulled away. "Go home? Have you lost all sense? Now is the time to act!" Ulyssa gaped at Judith. "But what are we to do with him? He is dead drunk!"

Holofernes snored loudly. She looked down at him with disgust. When she turned back, Judith was rummaging through Holofernes' things, looking desperately for something.

"What are you looking for?" Judith yanked out an enormous sword. "This!" she stated. In the dim light, its silver blade glinted and the jeweled handle sparkled like the stars. Emeralds, rubies, and sapphires were embedded in gold-and-silver vines that formed an intricate design. The blade itself had vines etched into it. Judith smiled triumphantly; Ulyssa swooned. "What are you going to do with that?" But Judith wasn't listening. She was standing over Holofernes' massive sleeping form. She held the weapon in her hands, pointing it to the heavens. She prayed out loud.

"O Lord of all might, look, in this hour, upon the work of my hands for the exaltation of Jerusalem. For now is the time to help your inheritance and carry out my undertaking for the destruction of the enemies who have risen against us."

Ulyssa watched with horror as Judith positioned herself above Holofernes' head. Springing forward, she grabbed Judith's arms and pulled the sword down. "Judith!" Judith stepped back, surprised that Ulyssa was being so forceful. Ulyssa didn't stop, though. "You of all people in this world should know the commandments of Yahweh! You, whom I have served for years with utmost respect, a respect born of the great admiration I have always had for your sound judgment and upright thoughts. Indeed, whenever I have listened to the priests and doctors speak of the just man, I have always thought of you as the personification of that one. And now! I see that I perhaps have been mistaken – or perhaps in truth you accidentally swallowed too much wine and it has obscured your reasoning." Judith stared blankly back at Ulyssa. "Dear servant, what are you getting at? I have the Lord's will to carry out and Israel to save. What is this qualm of conscience you are experiencing?"

"Qualm of conscience? Am I the only sane one here? Is killing a matter of conscience, or a matter of nature? Both I believe, although the latter weighs on us more heavily. Judith, in all respect, I cannot let you kill a man, no matter how evil he might be!" Ulyssa was red in the face, her eyes wide with fright. "Yahweh has said…" Her voice trailed off as Judith set the sword to the side and put her hands on Ulyssa's shoulders, looking her in the eyes.

"Yahweh has said, 'Thou shalt not kill.' You are right, but remember well what our fathers have spoken to us through the Holy Word. 'When in your own land you go to war against an enemy that is attacking you, you shall sound the alarm on the trumpets, and the Lord your God will remember you and save you from your foes.' Ulyssa, now is the time the Lord is saving us from our foes. Has he not in the past made use of mere men to carry out his will? Why not now – unworthy that I am, will he not make use of me? The Lord has brought me this far; he has delivered the enemy into our hands. When I crush the head of Holoferenes, I will finish the work the Lord has sent me to do. Ulyssa, I beg you, do not grow faint of heart! Help me, as I also fear! Our fear, though strongly felt, cannot be the cause of our failure to answer the Lord's call and save our people!"

Before Ulyssa could answer, Judith turned back to Holoferenes, and lifting the sword high she prayed aloud, "O Lord God of Israel, give me strength this day!" At the last word, she heaved downward in one swooping motion with her whole body. The sword sliced through his neck and blood spurted everywhere. Judith gave a cry of fright and her face drained of color. Ulyssa came forward to catch her lest she fall. Judith looked down at the blood now covering her dress and hands.

"Ulyssa," she said, staring horrorstruck at the bloody mess before her, "it didn't go through."

"What do you mean it didn't go through? He's dead! Can't you see?" Ulyssa was trying to pull the sword from Judith's hands. She looked about wildly, sure that someone had seen what Judith had done. She continued to pull at Judith, pleading with her to leave.

"No, Ulyssa, we need to finish." Her face was now green. She was trembling from head to foot. Ulyssa knew she had to get her out of there soon or they both would faint. She also knew Judith wouldn't leave until she had completed her task. Ulyssa glanced down at the body, closed her eyes in sickness, and grabbed Judith's arm.

"Judith, finish quickly! Don't waste time in weakness when you are justified by the Lord's grace!" Judith tore her eyes from Holofernes' body to look at her maid, who was frantic to leave. A light came into Judith's eyes, and Ulyssa knew she would go through. "Israel is waiting."

Judith nodded and began to pray again under her breath. Ulyssa closed her eyes this time as Judith put her heel on his head, turning it to the side. With one foot on his head to steady it and the other firmly planted on the ground, Judith lifted the sword once more, severing Holofernes' head with one last mighty swing. When Ulyssa heard the sword thud, she looked to see the blood flowing freely about their feet. It seeped into the rugs and formed a puddle. Holofernes' sword fell from Judith's hands. She, however, was far from fainting. With a renewed strength, she pulled the sheets from the bed. With Ulyssa's help, they wrapped the great general's body in them. Reaching up, Judith tore the glittering canopy from the bedposts. She picked up his ugly head by the hair, rolled it into the canopy, and then tucked her bundle into the basket of food Ulyssa had brought.

Judith swung the basket onto her arm and turned to Ulyssa. "Now we must go." Ulyssa couldn't have heard a better command. She took Judith by the arm, and together they rushed out of the tent. They hurried through the camp, darting from shadow to shadow, avoiding the watchmen roaming about. To the east, the sky was steadily growing lighter. It turned from deep blue to gray as they trekked through the camp that seemed to have grown since they last went through. At last the gate to the valley was in sight. They both began to run. As they passed by the post, a man jumped in front of them. Ulyssa ran into him, and Judith dropped the basket in fright.

"What are you doing? State your name!" the man shouted gruffly. They recognized the man who had stopped them when they had first surrendered themselves that very evening.

Ulyssa began to pray, sure that she had finally met her death. Judith took control. "Namak, it is us again. We are going to pray for the sunrise. You frightened us and made me upset my basket." She stooped down to pick it up, thanking God that nothing had fallen out.

Namak stepped back in contrition. "Forgive me! By Holofernes' order, you are to go out and pray." He stood at the gate and watched as they disappeared in the valley's tall grass that lined the river.

The sun was high above them by the time they made it to the gates of Bethulia. Ulyssa was drooping with fatigue, wondering where Judith's vigor was coming from. She had not stopped once in the hours of their trek through the valley and up to the mountain.

The great wooden gate loomed above them and the city seemed to be asleep. There was no noise coming through nor sign of life.

Judith called out, "Open, open the gates for us! God, our God is still with his people, to show his strength and power to Israel."

High above them, a head appeared through one of the turrets. Judith waved at him. His head disappeared and they heard some men shouting. Suddenly, Uzziah looked out from the turret.

"Uzziah, open the gate! It is I, Judith, with my faithful maid! The Lord has delivered the enemy to our hands!" Uzziah didn't respond but pulled his head back in. A few moments later, chains began to rumble as the gate was lifted.

The massive door folded up. Standing inside were Uzziah with the other magistrates and a guard of soldiers. They rushed out to the two women and hauled them into the city. As soon as they cleared the gate, the men pulling the chain let go and the gate came crashing down. Before the women could say anything, the men wrapped blankets around them and put them on horses to be carried farther in to the city. Ulyssa watched wide-eyed as they turned a corner and entered the square. Men were heaving sticks and logs into a huge pile in the center for a fire. As they worked, more men, women, and children began to gather in the afternoon sun. Everyone was amazed to see Judith and her maid, staring at their ragged appearance in disbelief. When it seemed that the entire city was gathered in the square, the magistrates called for silence.

A hush enfolded the people. Every eye was on Judith. Ulyssa turned to look at her as well and marveled at the sight. Gone were the bracelets and jewelry that had hung around her neck. In their flight, Judith had lost them. Her green tunic was lost as well, and her white robe was brown with dust and spattered with blood-stains. Her hands also told the story of the deed she had done. The veil that had covered her beautiful hair was hanging down her back. Her hair hung in limp clumps. The comb used to secure it was tangled up, hanging from some strands. Her makeup was smeared and only deepened the circles under her eyes. One of her sandals was missing. From head to foot, she looked horrendous, yet she stood and addressed the crowd with untiring confidence.

"Praise the Lord, people of Bethulia! Praise the Lord, Israel! The Lord our God has delivered the enemy into our hands this very day!" The crowd of people didn't move; they seemed hesitant to believe this raving woman. Judith turned to her basket and hefted out the canopy containing Holofernes' head. She unrolled it and grabbed his head by the hair, hoisting it high for everyone to see. The crowd gasped in horror and withdrew. A child in the front began to cry.

"Here is the head of Holofernes, general of the Assyrian army!" The uneasy silence erupted into cheers and shouts of joy and praise to the Lord. Judith held the canopy up in her other hand and shouted again, "And here is the canopy of his bed, upon which the Lord delivered him into the hands of a woman. Yes, my maid can bear witness that the Lord used my hand to bring this man to his doom. It was I who brought this great general to his ruin, and it was I whom the Lord chose to save Israel."

More gasps and cheers came from the crowd as they imagined the terrors the two women endured through the course of the night. One by one they began to drop to their knees, bowing down to praise Yahweh. They lifted their hands and voices singing songs of thanksgiving. They thanked him for saving them from their enemy by the hand of a woman. They shouted out, blessing her above every woman on earth.

Judith didn't heed their praises, though. She frowned out upon them as they celebrated. Ulyssa watched as she called out for silence again. It took longer, but after a few minutes, the crowd had settled down enough to listen to her. She began, "People of the Lord! The battle is not yet won. There is still much to do, for the Assyrian camp has yet to learn of their general's death. When they do find out, we must be ready to defeat them for good. But do not lose heart!"

Judith persisted. "Listen, my brothers. Do not lose heart, for the Lord has revealed to me what we must do to secure victory." The crowd seemed to lean forward to listen better. Judith picked up the head again to show to them. "We must take this head and hang it from the turret for every enemy that approaches to see. When the sun reaches its zenith, let all the able-bodied men rush out to meet the advance guard of the Assyrians. Make as though you were preparing to meet them in battle, but without charging them. When the Assyrians see you, they will rush to wake their general and find him dead. When they realize that they have been deceived by a woman, panic will seize them, and they will flee."

It didn't take much more for the men of Bethulia to be convinced. At once a tumult of activity filled the square. The captains and magistrates shouted to one another, calling out orders and enlisting able-bodied men. From nowhere came swords, armor, and helmets. They clanged together as the high sun glinted off their polished surfaces.

The men marched back to the city square, where the fire in the center was but embers and ashes. The group moved on toward the city gates with Judith following behind. When they reached the gate, instead of proceeding through, Judith and Uzziah went to climb the turret. Ulyssa followed and huffed up the steep and narrow stairs, which stopped suddenly and opened to a small room with a window. It was the same window she and Judith had called up to that morning. Ulyssa went to peek out of it and jumped back with a shout when she came face to face with Holofernes' decapitated head. Uzziah snorted in amusement, but Judith was too focused to notice. She moved to the window and looked to the rows upon rows of soldiers filed in front of the gate. They were all facing Judith in silence, waiting on her blessing. She pulled off her shawl and waved it out the window. A cry came from the captain and the soldiers made an abrupt turn toward the valley. They began to march.

❧

Bagoas was sitting down for his afternoon meal when a guard from the front post came crashing into his tent. "Where is the general? If he still sleeps, wake him! The Israelites have become so bold as to come out to meet us in battle."

Bagoas had been waiting for something like this. He jumped up and addressed the soldier vehemently, "They will be destroyed completely." He bounded out of his tent and went to awaken the general. He called from the door of his room before entering, knowing the mood Holofernes would be in after the previous night's carousing. No one answered. Again he called and waited for a reply. "He must be out dead," thought Bagoas. He pushed the tent flap back and charged in. "General Holofernes, wake up! The enemy is..." He stopped short when he saw the bed empty, its sheets and canopy missing. That is when he noticed the bundled, blood-soaked sheets on the floor. He gasped and ran forward. Grabbing an end of the sheet, he pulled until Holofernes' headless body rolled out.

Bagoas opened his mouth to scream, but no sound came out. He stood in silent horror, staring at the scene. The head was nowhere to be found. Finally finding his voice, he cried out and began to weep with loud, wailing sobs. Tearing his garments, he sat on the floor and put his head in his hands. Two captains came rushing in upon hearing the cries and moans. Bagoas stopped suddenly and growled, "The woman!" He pushed past the captains and ran to Judith's tent. He tore in to find it empty. He shouted in rage and ran out to the crowd of Assyrian leaders that was gathered to wait on their general's command. Bagoas, his face purple with wrath and streaked with tears, bellowed to the men, "The slaves have tricked us! One Hebrew woman has brought disgrace upon the whole house of King Nebuchadnezzar!" One of the soldiers dropped his sword; the rest began to fire out confused questions. Bagoas ordered silence, shouting that Holofernes was dead, killed by a single woman.

The men cried out and one by one they rent their tunics in despair. They wailed and moaned in humiliation at being duped as they were.

Soldiers emerged from their tents in various stages of preparation, to see what was happening. The news spread like a wave throughout the camp, striking each man with fear. Some began packing their belongings, posing to desert and flee to their homes. An unadvised assent rippled through the camp as each man decided to abandon post. With Holofernes dead, they scattered in all directions.

However, they did not take the remaining Israelites into account. Those Israelites were waiting in the hills and valley, as Uzziah had ordered them. The Assyrian army didn't stand a chance, and they were cut down in their dispersion.

All day long, the Israelites swept through the valley, filling it with the bodies of Assyrians. When the last soldiers were killed, the Israelites descended upon the camp. They raided it of every fine dish and jewel. Clothing, armor, gold, and grain were hauled back to Bethulia. When the only things left were tents, the camp was set afire. It burned bright in the night. Its flames shot up to the heavens, engulfing the corpses of Assyrians and reducing the camp to ashes. The glow could be seen from the turret where Judith and her maid waited.

When news finally came that the Assyrian threat was eliminated, Judith clasped her hands together and began to thank God in prayer and songs. Ulyssa cried from relief and from being reminded of God's protection.

From generation to generation, the story of Judith was told and retold. That very day was etched in Israel's history. Always accompanying the retelling is the song of Reuben. Upon meeting Judith and hearing the account of her victory, Reuben, the high priest of Jerusalem, sang a song of thanksgiving to the Lord and to Judith. "You are the exaltation of Jerusalem! You are the joy of Israel; you are the great pride of our nation! May the Almighty bless you forever!"

Queen Esther

"For I know well the plans I have in mind for you, says the Lord, plans for your welcome, not for woe! Plans to give you a future full of hope. When you call me, when you go to pray to me, I will listen to you. When you look for me, you will find me. Yes, when you seek me with all your heart, you will find me with you, says the Lord."

JEREMIAH 29:11-14

*I*n the midst of a great darkness that spread over the land, a dragon grew up from the earth. It was brown and hideous and breathed fire from its nose. Down the way another was born. It too was great and horrible. The black and silver scales that covered its flesh glinted in the darkness. The two caught sight of one another and charged. Each step they took crushed villages, towns, and cities full of people. They clashed into one another in a deafening noise while screams echoed throughout the land. They began to tear at one another's flesh, yet neither retreated. Advance after advance, they fought day and night. With noise, confusion, thunder and earthquake, there was tumult upon the earth. Every nation prepared for war and many died in affliction and distress. All fought against the nation of the righteous, who feared the threatening evils. In their turmoil, they cried out to God. And from their cry, as though from a tiny spring, there came a great river. There was abundant water, and then light came. The sun rose and the lowly were exalted and consumed those held in honor…

◌℘◌

"What do you mean she will not come?" King Ahasuerus bellowed at the messenger. "I have summoned Queen Vashti, and she must come at once." He slammed his fist down on the arm of his throne. "Does she not value her life?" The question echoed through the royal court like a condemnation.

The servant skittered off. Moments of heavy silence followed. The king ran his hand through his ruffled brown hair. Despite his athletic bearing, he sat slumped in his chair, brooding over the fool he was being made into. He strummed his fingers with one hand and rested his chin on the other. His bushy eyebrows were knit in contemplation while his mustache twitched every so often. Courtiers shifted from foot to foot. They hardly dared look at the king let alone one another.

Just as the uneasiness of the entire company was about to break its peak, the servant came rushing in, sliding to a stop and half bowed to the king. The servant stood, revealing his white face and shaking knees. The court held its breath. "M-m-majesty r-refuses, Sire."

Roaring in anger, the king flung his throne off the platform. Shouting curses and threats, he stomped out, calling his advisors to follow. Seven princes of Persia and Media scurried after the raving king.

He banged through the heavy wooden door to his private rooms and threw himself into his tall, gold-gilt chair. Breathing deeply, he said through his teeth, "What are we to do?"

The princes all looked at one another with darting eyes. Haman stepped forward, his back stick straight and head held high. He had a thin nose with large nostrils that flared when he spoke. His thin lips and squinty eyes made him look pinched. "Sire, today, not only to the king has Queen Vashti done wrong, but she also has harmed the entire kingdom." Haman stopped and drew in a dramatic breath. "Her act of disobedience to your command will be made known to all women. They in turn will believe that if the great queen can disregard her husband's command, then so too can they." He nasally voice grew as his words gathered force. "There will be contempt and wrath in plenty. Chaos will cover the nation!"

He spat out the last words. He stopped, drew in another breath, smoothed down his hair, and began again. "What needs to be done is this." He leaned forward and spoke more softly. The other princes and the king leaned forward, too. "If it so please the king, let a royal decree go out saying that Queen Vashti, for her disrespect, will no longer be allowed into the presence of the king. Her place shall be taken by one more suitable than herself." A gasp escaped one of the princes. He lowered his eyes as the king looked up from under his eyebrows. King Ahasuerus stood up, stomped his foot, and said, "It will be done!"

Dispatches of translators and scribes came bustling in with their scrolls and writing utensils flying. In a flourish they began scribbling away as Haman reiterated the king's decree in his presence. Once they had their messages and destinations down, they bustled out and were sent to every province to proclaim that every man is lord of his own house and all who belong to it.

ⵏ

That same week, on the other side of the capital, a quieter scene played out. Mordecai watched from the doorway as his niece spun wool, deftly moving her fingers. It had only been four months since she had taken up the task, and already she had it mastered. The memory of finding her hands bandaged due to the beginner's experience of pricked fingers caused him to smile. Pushing the memory aside, he cleared his throat. Esther looked up from her work and smiled. Once again, Mordecai was caught by the similarity she bore to his brother. The green eyes, the wavy hair and full smile – it was all the same. Unlike her father though, she had the charm of her mother. Without even trying, she could spin a story an hour long and have everyone's attention the entire time. More than her stories, however, she could listen. She listened to anyone and everyone who came to seek her advice. From old to young, there was many a woman who sought her company. It was a rare moment to find her alone as she was now. Mordecai smiled as Esther rose to greet her uncle.

"You look serious today, Uncle. Is there something on your mind?" Esther asked, looking intently at him, studying him closely. He shook his head, looking more tired than usual. Esther thought he looked older. She took his hand and led him to the terrace chair. Once seated, she knelt down and began to remove his sandals.

"Esther," he chided softly, "that is a servant's work." She just smiled and continued to bathe his feet. When she had wiped them dry, she looked up at him. He sighed again, and looking away from her, he began to speak. "Do you remember the last decree the king sent?" She nodded. "Well, someone must take Queen Vashti's place." He stopped and looked at her. Her eyes betrayed her puzzlement as to where he was headed.

Mordecai stood up and began to pace the terrace. He stopped at one end and breathed in deeply, ready to say something, then shook his head and continued pacing. Esther stood up and watched him, her eyebrows knit together in concern. So intent was she on her uncle's disturbance that she failed to notice or admire the beauty of the setting day. Streaks of orange, brilliant pink and red cut through low-lying clouds and filled the terrace with flaming light. The green azalea bush glowed purple in the dusk.

Finally, running his hand through his hair, Mordecai stopped and faced his adopted daughter. His face dropped at the sight of her concern. She looked so young at only seventeen. But what was age to a king? "Esther...." His voice cracked. Mordecai moved closer to her and took her hand in between his. He cleared his throat. "Esther, you have been summoned to the king's harem to be among those presented to him in a year's time." Esther froze and then moved to sit down. The red light hid her face, which was draining of color. Mordecai, afraid she would faint, jumped forward to sit beside her. "Esther, it's just for a year. The king will have nearly one hundred women to choose from. What are the chances he would choose you?" Esther closed her eyes and leaned back.

"It's strange," she said softly, "but this morning I was praying, and I had an intuition that something would happen today." She sat up and looked at Mordecai. "Perhaps the Lord is preparing us for something, Uncle."

Mordecai looked away and brushed at his eye, clearing his throat. Standing up, he took Esther by the hands and promised her he would always be close to her. He kissed the top of her head and went inside. Esther was left alone with her thoughts; they swirled around and around until she too went in to help prepare supper. The sun had already set in a flaming burst of rays. Now, the deep purple and black of night were descending upon the garden.

That night, Esther stood in the middle of the room, pointing out which things to keep, which to give away and where everything went. Mordecai sat on a chair in the corner, watching and remembering the day he had brought her into his house…

"Mordecai, you are an unmarried man! What do you think you are doing, taking in a young girl to raise?" His housemaid had been furious about his decision, but she didn't understand the bond of brotherhood he felt toward Esther's father.

"Rachel," he reprimanded her, "she is my niece. I know it seems unlikely, but I believe the Lord is calling me to be both fahter and mother to her." He paused, considering the words he had just spoken. They surprised him even as he voiced them, but now that he had said them, he was more determined than ever. "I'm making this decision on my own responsibility. If I don't take her in, she will be thrown to the streets and will surely die." He looked down at the sleeping four-year-old child. She was beautiful even at so young an age. "No, Rachel," he said in a softer voice, "I will raise her as my daughter. She will have what she needs. I will surround her with maids and nurses. This is as it must be."

"Uncle, the convoy is here. Uncle?" Mordecai had fallen asleep. Esther must have brought the blanket that covered him. Morning light, soft and pure, filled the room. He could hear the palace eunuch in the atrium.

The old man stood up and embraced his daughter. She hugged him back fiercely. When she pulled away, he saw tears in her eyes. She grabbed his calloused hands in her own and kissed them. "Thank you for everything you have done for me. I couldn't have asked for a better father!"

Mordecai continued to hold her hands in his and looked her straight in the eyes. "My daughter, listen to me if ever you do in your life. Don't tell anyone of your Jewish descent." Her eyes welled with tears of fear and she asked, "Why do you tell me this?" Mordecai shook his head. "The time will come when it will prove well for it to be known. But for the time being, let it remain secret. Do you understand?" Esther nodded. Mordecai let go of her hands. She turned and walked to the front door. The palace servants had already packed her belongings. The door closed behind her, and she was gone.

❦

"Esther, don't forget anything you've been taught, okay? Don't forget that you always clasp your hands when you are nervous. So don't clasp your hands, okay? And don't forget that this garment is long in the back so don't trip on it, okay? Esther, are you listening to me? Esther?" Hegai, the chief eunuch in charge of the king's harem looked at the girl. She was staring off into the distance, wringing her hands. The third time he called her name she looked at him. "What? Right. Stop clasping my hands. Right…." She put her hands down and composed her features, smoothing down her garments as well. With one hand she touched her hair, which had been done up elegantly as a queen's. *A queen.* That is what she had been in training to become for the past ten months. They had been ten months of missing Mordecai while instructing herself to become what she believed God wanted her to be. That was the sole reason she gave herself to her lessons and courses with more vigor than all the others in preparation with her. And that was the reason she had won Hegai's favor.

When the time came for her to be presented, Hegai took her personally to the king's court along with seven other women. They were the last ones to be presented to the king. So far, no one had provoked so much as a raised eyebrow from him. The king seemed completely disinterested in the whole matter. Today was different though. Hegai knew today was the day. He just hoped she was ready enough.

As they approached the king's court, he kept whispering fierce reminders in her ear. He wanted everything to go perfectly. She continued to nod but had already tripped twice on her overly long garment. As they entered the court, Hegai made sure Esther went last. He knew the others didn't stand a chance and he wanted to make sure everything was in place. The courtroom buzzed with excited voices and gossipers who would spread news of the king's day to all corners of the city.

When at last her name was called, Esther straightened up and brushed off Hegai's hands that were fixing her already perfect hair. She walked forward with stately grace and ease. The entire courtroom fell silent. She went up the aisle and bowed to the king. Standing up, she made sure to avoid eye contact, as she had been instructed. She couldn't help though, when the king stood up. She looked up. He came forward to examine her more closely. Embarrassed, she dropped her gaze, but the king caught her chin in his hand and raised her head to be level with his. Esther saw the room start to swirl. She was dizzy from fear of this great man. Just before she felt she would pass out, the king turned and went back to his place. Hegai came up to escort her out.

"You're his," he whispered as they hurried back to the harem. Then her thoughts, which had been frozen from the fear she still felt, began to twirl with the reality of Hegai's words. She stopped dead on the path. "I can't be queen. What about my uncle?" Hegai turned to see that tears were filling her eyes. They glistened in the evening sun. Hegai sighed.

"Child, there comes a time in a person's life when she has to break away from the ties of childhood. This is a gift the gods have favored you with. Now it is your turn to answer maturely and with the queenly grace you already possess. Don't you see this is what you were made for? The gods have ordained it to be so." He stopped to see if his words were sinking in. They were; she was listening. "How many others were presented to the king? There have been so many that have come through without even a sneeze from him. And what happened when you came? He came down to you! Don't you see it is a sign that the gods themselves are coming down to you this day? So many now are being eaten alive by jealousy of you. And the king – he is enamored. He won't sleep tonight; he will be thinking of you!"

Esther started walking slowly again back to the harem. "Hegai, do you believe that God, whichever god it might be, really plans these things to be as they are?"

"With all my heart."

Again she stopped to look her friend in the eyes. She saw he was sincere. "Very well then, Mordecai will understand." Hegai hesitated at the front steps, and Esther turned to him. "What is it?" she asked. He lifted his hand and rubbed the back of his neck, looking off to the side. "Esther, I *know* Mordecai will understand. He has come to the harem every day since you arrived. He has kept a close eye on you the entire time, seeing to it that you fared well. Yesterday, when he came, he told me he had dreamt that the king would choose you." Esther nodded in understanding. It didn't surprise her that Mordecai would be there, nor that he would be revealed her destiny in a dream. God could do whatever he wanted to make his will known. "Thank you, Hegai. I am going to retire now." With that she entered the harem and went to bed for the night. How much she slept, however, even she couldn't say.

Hegai stayed outside in the garden, strolling though its paths. Mordecai would come by soon to see how the presentation had gone, if he hadn't already heard from the gossip circles. "What a strong woman this young girl is," he mused. "I wonder what the gods have in store for the king more than for this girl." He was confident she would adjust quickly to palace life.

☙

"Uncle! What are you doing here?"

"Hush, hush. You are a queen now, no longer a child who can come running to her father's arms when she sees him!" Esther blushed and tried to hold in her excitement. It was the first time she had been able to see him since the brief visit before her marriage. Glancing about, he lowered his head and motioned her closer. "Esther, I am here to tell you that the guards at the gate are plotting against the king's life. You must reveal their plans to the king so he may take proper action. Tell him in my name of these things… Don't be frightened, daughter." Esther looked long at her uncle. "Thank you for saving my husband's life. Anything you ask of me, I will have it done." Mordecai smiled at her. "I'm glad to hear concern for the one you're married to." Esther's eyebrows shot up. "Well of course, it is my duty to look after him. But, you go on! I'll see you later." Esther kissed his hand and hurried down the long cool corridor of the palace.

Three days later, the guards at the gate were hanged in the gallows after their plots against the king's life were discovered.

☙

Esther was in the dining hall, meeting with the cooks about a menu for an upcoming feast the king was planning. They sat around her bickering about ways to roast the lamb. Esther looked

54

about her at the majesty she was seated in. Great alabaster columns lifted the ceiling high above her. Curtains covering the windows were billowing out as a strong breeze filled with the smell of sea salt blew in. The distant cry of gulls could be heard as they swooped in and out of the water to gather their breakfast. The mahogany table before her had been shipped in from distant forests of lands uninhabited by civil men. It was long, and its polished surface reflected the light that bounced in through the open doors at the end of the hall. It was a far cry from the simple yet sturdy table she had grown up at.

Everything was still foreign to her, even after three months of living there. Most foreign to her was the man whom she had married. It had been nearly thirty days since she had been summoned to his court, and she was learning that it wasn't a normal relationship that a queen has with a king. That didn't faze her as much as actually being called to there. It was a big, imposing room with heavy marble columns and shining polished floors that reflected the burning fires that lit the room. And then there were the courtiers. They glittered like wheat fields in the sun, decked in their emerald-and-gold jewelry. The way they spoke behind their hands and whispered when she entered unnerved her. Yes, she was glad not to be called to that place.

A sigh escaped as she stared into the silver platter in front of her. The glistening crown on her head seemed to mar her reflection. "So many envy me for this crown, but what I wouldn't give to toss it to the sea and return to my uncle… to my people." She shook her head. It never helped to let herself be taken by thoughts of what could have been. "I am doing as the Lord has chosen for me; in that I am joyful."

As she stood up from her meeting, one of her handmaids came running in. "Saria," Esther asked, "what is it that has you nearly in tears?" The poor girl burst out in a wail, "Majesty, I hate to be the one that has to tell you such dreadful news! The others made me draw lots and I was chosen. Please don't make me say it, though! It's just too terrible. No, I can't tell you!" She turned to run out, but Esther caught her by the wrist.

"Saria, what is it? I command you to tell me." The girl began to weep in earnest, "Well, Mordecai, your uncle, he-he's out at the palace gate calling for you. He won't come in because he's in sackcloth and ashes. It's such a pitiful sight. It made me cry just to see it, Majesty. He kept wailing about his people who were being put to death. Your eunuch went to try to get him to dress so he could at least come in to see you, but he refused. Instead, he gave him a copy of a decree the king sent out. It's just all so terrible. Majesty, I didn't want to tell you this but they made me even though I begged them not to. And now you're distressed! Majesty, please don't be upset by this. I'm sure something good will come." Esther let go of the girl and sat down. The girl ran out crying.

Esther stared blankly in front of her, trying to sort through her thoughts. Hegai, her eunuch, came in. "Majesty!" he said in a breathless voice. "Majesty, forgive poor Saria. I had no idea they would send that girl here to tell you. I was on my way and ran into her just outside the door. Look here – I have the letter from Mordecai."

Esther took it from him. The paper shook in her hands as she read the decree issued for the destruction of all Jews. It was signed and sealed by her husband, the king. The paper fluttered to the ground as she brought her hand to her mouth. "How could he do this?" she whispered. Hegai only shook his head sadly. "The king is bombarded by advisers all day long. It is easy that he could have been manipulated into signing something with no idea of what it contained." Esther stared down at the paper on the floor. "What about Mordecai? What is he to do?"

Hegai cleared his throat. Esther looked up at him. He was staring at her expectantly. "What's that look mean, Hegai?" she asked. He looked down at his hands and began to speak. "You aren't a girl in the harem anymore, Esther. I cannot instruct you to do this or that any longer…" He paused and Esther stood up. "Hegai, the crown on my head tells everyone I am queen, but inside, I feel the same as a girl in need of help. My people are in trouble. Help me decide what to do." Hegai looked up at her and bowed his head. "Are you sure you want the advice I am going to give?" he asked. Esther started to wring her hands. "Y-Yes, I can handle it."

"Alright. But first, sit down." Once she was seated, Hegai stood and, taking the letter in his hands, began, "I think Mordecai sent this so that you could do something." Esther sank in her chair. "But what can I do? I am just a-" "A queen," Hegai interrupted. "That is who you are, even if you don't feel it. You are the wife of the man who signed this decree whether he knew what it contained or not." Esther swallowed. "Yes, but I haven't been summoned to his court for more than a month. We both know that to go before him uninvited means death."

Hegai shook his head. "Majesty, you told me to speak openly, so I will. Mordecai understands your situation here and told me to relay this message to you." Esther nodded. "Queen Esther, your people are being put to death. If you had never been brought to this palace, if your God had never destined you for this place of honor, you would be in danger of death as well. The danger you face in going before the king uninvited is no less than the danger your people face this very moment." Esther was growing white. "Believe me, if you keep silent at such a time as this, relief and deliverance will rise for the Jews from another quarter, but you and your father's household will perish. Who knows whether you have not come to the kingdom for such a time as this?"

Esther trembled from head to foot. She walked over to Hegai, took the paper from him, and read through it again. Looking up, she said, "Tell Mordecai to send word to all my people. They are to fast and offer supplication for three days now as I myself will. On the third day, I will go before the king even though it is against the law. And if I perish, I perish." Standing up, she left Hegai staring at her.

Queen Esther fled to her chambers where she and her maids stripped themselves of every jewel and clothed themselves in sackcloth. She covered herself in ashes and fasted for three days and three nights. Mordecai likewise called together all the Jewish communities, explaining to them the queen's plan. Overcome with hope at the prospect of having one of their own interceding for them, they all took to fasting and prayer.

Ↄ

"Alone. Lord, I am alone, with no helper. My husband has turned against my people, even if unknowingly. My only helper is you. And yet, you are God. Who am I to call on you to assist me? I would never turn to you for the distance between us. I am a lowly creature, and you, my Creator. I have become a queen against all that is pleasing to me. From the moment I took the crown upon my head, I have suffered the weight of it. My only joy has been in wearing it for you. You are my Creator and the Lord of my people and of Israel. That is why I find the daring to approach you. From the time I could sit upon my uncle's lap, he has told me stories of your steadfast fidelity to your people. And I, I who fear so much, come before you to beg you take pity. Listen to the prayer of your servant. Remember me, Lord. Make yourself known in this time of affliction. O King of the gods and Master of all dominion, give me courage! Put eloquent speech in my mouth. Turn a man's heart of hate into one of pity for my people. Save us by your mighty hand. We call on you, we who are alone with no helper but yourself. Hear our prayer, Lord of Hosts."

⠀⠀⠀⠀⠀⠀⠀⠀⠀⠀⠀⠀⠀⠀⠀⠀⠀⠀*CB*

⠀⠀The low murmurs from the courtiers crept under Esther's skin. She hadn't even entered the vast room and already it was too much. She stood at the threshold, hidden behind a large fern encased in a vase. She breathed deeply, trying to calm her nerves. It was to no avail, though; her stomach only knotted all the more every time her thoughts returned to the door she was to go through.

⠀⠀She leaned closer to the ferns and for the first time recognized their smell. She remembered that smell, and it brought her back to her uncle's garden. She loved to go there and look at the fish in his little pond. Once, when she was eight, Mordecai had come out to call her in because a storm was approaching. As he came, lightening thundered in the distance. Esther used to be terrified of lightening. Thinking she was alone, she sprang up to run inside only to collide into her uncle. He looked down at her frightened face and swept her up in his arms. "Don't be frightened, child. Don't you know I came here to bring you in?" Esther only clapped her hands over her ears as another boom echoed through the sky. Suddenly rain came pelting down in torrents. Mordecai ran in with Esther in his arms. They were drenched when they entered.

⠀⠀⠀⠀⠀⠀⠀⠀⠀⠀⠀⠀⠀⠀⠀⠀⠀⠀*CB*

⠀⠀A group of guards marched by. Their footsteps echoed through the empty hallway and brought Esther back to the task before her. "Don't be frightened." The words remained in her heart. Mordecai had never let Esther fall into harm. He had brought her up and protected her, sacrificing his own possibilities of ever marrying or having a family of his own. "Now," she thought, "now it's my turn to do something for him."

A hush fell over the king's court once they realized the queen had entered. The king was distractedly listening to an accountant rattling off the year's expenses. The accountant's voice trailed off as he saw the queen. The king continued to play with the tassel tied to his scepter. Everyone there knew the laws of court. They held their breath in terror and excitement. The king stopped playing with the tassel and looked up at the sudden silence. His surprise turned to shock as he saw his wife standing before him with her head held defiantly high.

The king's face flushed with humiliation. "Wasn't one disobedient wife enough in one lifetime?" he though. His humiliation turned to white-hot anger. He slowly stood up.

Esther clasped her hands together, but her face remained resolute. Her heart was frozen with fear. She opened her mouth to state the speech she had spent all night running through in her head. She tried to say something, but the room was spinning.

The king watched as Esther turned shades paler. She faltered when she tried to speak and kept wringing her hands. Before a word could escape her mouth, she swooned, crumpling to the ground in a heap. The hall of people gasped. Something about the fright he saw on her face moved the king. For the first time, he felt sorry for her. Rushing forward, he threw aside the accountant who was almost hanging on his shoulder. "She is frightened of me!" he thought as he knelt at her side. He sat on the ground and lifted her limp form into his arms. He looked into her lovely face and felt a pang in his heart. "How could I have forgotten about her? Why have I not devoted more time to her? " She came to, and upon seeing the nearness of the king, fainted once again.

The king looked up at the servants crowding around. This time he let his anger loose. "Get out of here! Can't you see you are overcrowding her! Someone get a basin of water!" Before he finished shouting, a cool rag was placed in his hand. He dabbed the queen's forehead. She moaned softly and opened her eyes once again.

Her eyes focused on the king's face. Her breathing grew short and her eyes darted about, as if seeking an escape. The king spoke. "What is it, Esther?" he asked. "What has frightened you so? Do not fear. I am your brother and you shall not die."

Esther sat up and looked at the king, still hesitating. "My king, I saw you like an angel of the Lord and my heart was shaken by fear." Again, her face began to drain of color. The king, fearing she would faint again, began to speak. "Esther, Esther, have no fear. Tell me what it is you are seeking. Anything you wish will be granted you."

Esther became aware of the silence that reigned in the great hall. She peered around at all the strange, glittering faces watching the interplay between her and the king. She leaned forward and said in a lower voice, "If it please you, come to dinner with me today, and I will make my request. Bring your advisers. Please, my lord."

Ahasuerus, king of Susa and the surrounding countries, turned to a servant and said, "Gather my chief advisers and call them to dinner with the queen at once." The servant rushed out and three handmaids came to help Esther to her room. The king left her with them and departed for his own chambers, leaving the great hall to the gossip of the courtiers.

In her room, Esther sat with closed eyes as her maids fixed her hair. She didn't speak to them nor seem to want them to speak to her. Thinking of the king, she wondered at his seeming change of heart. "When was the last time he looked at me like that? There was a type of tenderness there," she thought. Unable to figure out what had happened, she shrugged to her reflection and thanked Yahweh for answering her prayer. When finished, she nodded and stood. Thirty minutes later, Esther was at table with him and his seven advisers.

For the most part, the king continued to talk of business affairs with his advisers. "Haman, tell me what ever came of the order I issued last through you?" Haman, the chief adviser, stood. "Please, my king, the issue sent to the chastisement of a certain unruly people is in the process of taking effect." Esther froze; she looked at Haman, who was beaming at the king. Esther looked to the king, who nodded distractedly, his thoughts moving on to other matters. Esther jumped up from her chair and pointed her finger at the chief adviser, shouting, "You!"

Every head snapped up in surprise at the queen's outburst. Haman was staring with wide eyes at the woman pointing across the table at him. Seeing the embarrassment in her husband's face, Esther dropped her hand. "Queen Esther," the king said slowly. "What is it?" She turned red. "Nothing, my king," she answered. "It is just that I want to… to…" She groped around in her mind for an excuse or a way to reveal Haman's misdeeds. An idea occurred to her. She looked up with a carefully placed smile. "I just wanted to invite my king and Haman to dine with me again tomorrow. Then I shall ask the request you have chosen to grant me." The king smiled at seeing that Esther had calmed down. He rose and came over to her chair. Putting his hand on her shoulder, he said, "Haman, we shall dine with the queen tomorrow and then grant her request." He then turned and left the dining hall, his footsteps echoing across the silent room. Esther looked around at the strangers she had been left with. Deeply embarrassed, she stood and left as well, the whole time evading Haman's glowing gaze.

ଔଔ

"Zeresh, come rejoice with your husband who has found favor in the eyes of the king and his queen!" Haman came bursting into his wife's garden. She looked up in delight. "What is this? Tell me what has made you so high-spirited?" Haman stood before the chair Zeresh lounged in and related all that had come about that day. She, too, grew excited at the great honor that was being shown to their family. "Could anything be greater? There is nothing that can dampen our happiness!"

ଔଔ

"The king is calling for you to read to him from the book of memorable deeds done in his reign. Bring out the chronicles for the king who cannot sleep." A servant came scurrying in with three scrolls in his arms. Pulling out a low stool, he sat upon it and, clearing his throat, began to read. He read on and on, telling stories of people the king had helped, of widows and orphans. He read of people who had done great services to the king, of soldiers and countrymen. The king listened attentively from his bed. The servant then told of a man who had once saved the king's life by revealing a plot two men had devised against him. At this, the king sat up in his bed. "Who is this man you tell me of?"

"Mordecai is his name. He is a Jew, Sire," answered the servant. "And has he been given a reward for his service to my life?" the king asked. The servant stared back blankly. "Do you know anything besides what you read?" the king asked in frustration. The servant shook his head. The king threw him out and finally fell asleep, thinking all the while of Mordecai.

The next morning, Haman came in to greet the king during his breakfast. "Aha, Haman, you will know!" the king said. "What should be done to a man whom the king pleases to honor?" Haman puffed his chest out and bowed low, his nose nearly touching the ground. He thought, "What blessings the king already is planning to honor me with!" Clearing his throat in a dignified manner, he began, "For the one the king should wish to honor, let royal robes that the king himself has worn be brought to him and placed about his shoulders. Let a horse the king himself has ridden be brought for him to ride upon. And let that man be conducted through the main square with a herald proclaiming, 'Thus will it be done to the man whom the king delights to honor!'"

The king nodded in hearty agreement. "Very well, Haman. Make haste then and gather the robes and the horse!" Haman nodded, trying to hold back a smile. The king continued, "Once you have retrieved those, do all that you have said, not leaving out a thing!" Haman nodded again. With itching anticipation he asked, "My liege, whom, in your great munificence, have you chosen to honor so?" The king gave a hearty laugh. "I forgot to tell you!" he said. Haman joined him in laughing. The king stated, "Mordecai, the Jew! The one who saved my life!"

Haman's laugh turned to a cough. His face went white. "Mordecai?" he asked. "Yes! Mordecai!" the king repeated. "Make haste now and inform me later." And the king left Haman alone, staring in seething anger and envy. He took the edge of the low table laden with fruit and turned it over in a fury. Figs and grapes went spinning across the marble floor. Haman stomped on them as he left the room.

"Zeresh! Zeresh! Where is a woman when her husband calls for her? Zeresh!" Haman bellowed through his house, only to find Zeresh in the garden, asleep under a tree. "Wake up, woman!" She jumped up in fright and confusion. "What is it? Why do you yell as if the world were ending?"

"The world is ending for us! Do you know what I had to do this afternoon?" Zeresh looked alarmed. "What?" she asked. Haman paced back and forth in front of her with his arms flailing as he thundered out the humiliation of having to herald Mordecai's honor before all the people in the great square. When at last he finished, he sank into a garden chair and, putting his head in his hands, sighed deeply. "Your husband is a failure."

"My lord." A servant had come out with a palace guard behind him. The guard stepped forward. "I am here to escort you to dinner, where the king and queen are waiting." Haman sighed in exasperation. "I had forgotten about that in my fury." Zeresh looked at him inquisitively, narrowing her eyes, as if trying to give him a sign. Haman shrugged to show he didn't understand. Zeresh approached, took him by the elbow and, pulling him away from the guard, whispered in his ear, "This is your chance! Tonight in the dinner, you can lie to the king and queen, telling them Mordecai has let the honor go to his head and is plotting to usurp the throne! Ask to have him hanged in the gallows. That will put an end to the Jew, and then the king will honor you for saving his life!"

Haman nodded as she unfolded her plot. She pulled away, and he saw her serious face. Her mind was set, as was his. He leaned forward to embrace her. "You are a brilliant woman!" With that, he left with the guard for the palace.

❧

The dinner had been going on for quite some time now, and still Queen Esther had not presented her request. Haman was becoming agitated, for he wanted to bring up the "bad news" after Esther was finished. Finally, the wine came around, and the king turned to Esther. "Tell me now, what is your petition, Queen Esther? Tell me your request. Even if it be half the kingdom, I will grant it you."

Esther stood and came over to the king's chair. She knelt beside it. "If I have found favor in your sight, O King, and if it please the king, let my life be given me at my petition, and my people at my request. For we are sold, me and my people, to be destroyed, to be slain, and to be annihilated." Haman had been drinking from his wine goblet. Upon hearing the queen, he inhaled wine and began to cough. His face went red as Esther continued, "If we had been sold merely as slaves, men and women, I would have held my peace; for our affliction is not to be compared with the loss of the king."

The king looked down at her with a stern face. "And who is it that would presume to do this to your people? For in doing so to your people, he does to my own."

Esther stood then and looked at Haman, who was slowly sinking in his chair, "It is he, the wicked Haman, your chief adviser, my king."

The king looked in surprise at Haman. "You, Haman?" The adviser began to stammer, "K-k-king, my- my liege, I can ex-explain." The king rose, knocking his chair over in his anger. Betrayal shone in his eyes, and without saying a word, he stormed from the room. Esther in the meantime sat down.

Once the king was gone, Haman jumped up and fell before the queen. "Majesty," he begged with pity, "have mercy! If I have lost favor with the king, only death awaits me, for outside this palace, I am nothing!" Esther shook her head sadly. Growing desperate, he grabbed her arms and begged all the more, "I beg you." At that moment the king entered again to the dining hall. A wave of fury swept through his shuddering frame. "Have you not insulted the king enough that now you attack his queen?" he asked in a quiet voice. His livid features belied the storm he held within.

Haman moved his lips soundlessly, glancing between the queen and the king, dumbfounded at how fate had betrayed him. He released his grip and stepped away from the queen, stumbling backward to the floor. The king snapped his fingers. Two burly guards came in and picked Haman up, perceiving the king's unspoken command. Haman moaned desperately as he was dragged from the king's presence.

Silence settled into the hall, a stark contrast to all that had occurred. Esther still sat where she was with her head in her hands. The king came over and sat beside her. "Are you alright?" he asked. Esther looked over the top of her hands and nodded, her eyes brimming with tears. He put his arm around her and she began to cry in earnest. "It's all right now. It's all right," he kept repeating. "I believe your God has heard your plea. It's all right."

The following day, Esther received a scroll from Mordecai.

"These things have come from God, for I remember the dream that I had concerning these matters, and none of them has failed to be fulfilled. The tiny spring that became a river, and there was light and the sun and abundant water – the river is you, Esther, whom the king married and made his queen. The two dragons are Haman and I. The nations are those that gathered to destroy the name of the Jews, and my nation, this is Israel, who cried out to God and was saved. The Lord saved his people. The Lord has delivered us all from these evils. God has done great signs and wonders. Blessed be the name of the Lord!"

Susanna

"Set me as a seal on your heart, as a seal on your arm; for stern as death is love, relentless as the nether world is devotion; its flames are a blazing fire. Deep fires cannot quench love, nor do floods sweep it away."

SONG OF SONGS 8:6-7

"Dear Susanna, my lovely young wife! Tell me, how have you longed for your husband these weeks since I have been absent?" Joachim extended his arms to greet Susanna. His gesture of openness was all Susanna needed to smile in response. Her smile reached her brown eyes and the first hint of a wrinkle creased them. Reaching out, she walked into his embrace. She was at least a head taller than her husband, with brown hair that she kept swept up under her veil. Her soft and graceful features were accented by demure bearing and manner of dress. Pulling back, she said, "Joachim, I am pleased to have you safe at home. The house is empty without you. Even the servants seemed down."

Joachim chuckled in delight, stroking his short-trimmed beard. It once had been a brilliant red, a rare color for his race; however, now it was duller and sprinkled with strands of gray.

"Don't be such a woman. This household is huge; surely one person does not make a difference."

A voice came from the corner of the room. "It is your presence that makes a difference, sir." From the shadows of a potted plant came a gaunt, hollow face with pale-blue deep-set eyes. The man was tall and thin with long arms that hung like limp rope at his sides. Everything about him was long and thin. Dressed in dark gray, he managed to blend in with the shadows. His nose was crooked, most likely broken when he was young. Sparse hair was neatly slicked down over his high forehead. Persivius, one of the town's chief judges, bowed stiffly to Joachim.

Joachim chuckled once again. "Persivius, you old goat! I didn't see you enter! What are you doing lurking about in those dark corners?"

Without the least expression, the servant answered, "I thought I heard a rodent, sir."

"A rodent? In my house?" Joachim stood up from the divan he had been reclining on and searched the corner from which Persivius had come. Persivius watched him moving about with a disdainful look. His eyes didn't dart as some did; rather, he methodically took things in, surveying everything calmly and precisely. Susanna shifted in her seat when he turned to look at her. Not finding anything, Joachim straightened up and moved over to the open window. A soft evening breeze fluttered in, bringing with it the scent of lilacs and mastic trees from the garden.

Persivius continued to look at Susanna with dull, lifeless eyes. She rubbed away the chill that had crept into her arms. Joachim turned back and noticed her shiver.

"Are you cold, my love? Persivius, fetch a lad to light the fire."

Persivius drifted from the room. Susanna watched him leave, sitting back and uncrossing her arms as he disappeared. Joachim brought a blanket to put around her shoulders and sat down next to her. "So tell me, Susanna! What did you do to pass your time?" Before she could bring her thoughts back to what her husband was saying, Persivius came back into the room to answer for her. "She spent most of it at the synagogue, depleting your wealth with her contributions."

With a jovial laugh and putting his arm around Susanna, Joachim said, "Yes! That sounds like my pious wife! That is why I love her though, Persy! At least one of us fears the Lord and lives according to the Law. But Persivius, before I forget, would you make sure the camels are being taken care of? Then you can call it a day. We are celebrating my return!"

Persivius bowed to Joachim and left. Susanna watched the way the fire lit her husband's graying hair to the red it was failing to be. "Joachim, you as well are a pious man." He turned to look at her, surprised that she picked up on the comment. Susanna nodded. "If I didn't believe it before, I do now. When you were away I realized how honored you are by the people of Babylon. When the master of the house is away, they come to the mistress. I was bombarded by our brother Jews seeking your counsel."

Joachim shifted in his seat. "You shouldn't have had to deal with that. Where were Persivius and Cranitus? They are the elder judges here to govern them." His brow creased in concern. "I know! They must have been busy preparing for my return!"

Once again, Joachim stared back into the fire with a contented smile. Susanna now was the one with concern. She shrugged her shoulder. "Yes, that must have been it." Suddenly she stood up. Joachim looked up to her with a questioning look. Susanna said, "Those people who came to see me will be coming in droves tomorrow once they discover you've returned. You'd better retire early to have strength to greet them."

Joachim gave a hearty laugh. "Susanna! What would I do without you? You take such good care of me, your old husband."

&

The next morning at six, the house was already abuzz with people milling about in the front rooms discussing and bickering over Rome, the weather, and the quality of Egyptian wool. Susanna graciously entertained those she could, the wives. She even managed to send some slaves off with baskets of sweet breads. By noon, however, she was exhausted.

As soon as the crowd of people had decreased to a few straggling guests who were hoping to be invited on to lunch, Susanna slipped out the side door into the garden. Breathing in deeply, she closed her eyes and then opened them to the spacious yard. Trees lined the walls on all three sides, invisible due to the vines and creeping flowers that grew in between the trees. The foliage was broken only by the single gate that led to the street. In the center was a pond that Joachim had dug for Susanna the year before. Water lilies floated in it. Right next to it was the great mastic tree, the only one in the garden. The rest of the space was taken up by random benches set up in coves of lilac bushes and trellises of grapevines.

Susanna meandered through, enjoying the sound of the birds, and stopped to question the gardener about his work, oblivious to the shadows of a side room in the house, where a man and his boy moved to the window.

The man peered out of the curtained window, muttering to himself. The boy watched him uncomfortably. Daniel despised the low nature of Cranitus' behavior. "His poor wife," he thought. "He doesn't even care for her anymore." When Cranitus remained at the window for too long, Daniel decided to intervene. He cleared his throat.

"Master, your wife told me to remind you to come back immediately after the meetings. You have a feast to attend tonight in honor of your cousin's wedding." Daniel watched his master as he gazed out the window. He was of medium set with a bald head and beady eyes. His cheeks were pink and fleshy. His whole head turned blotchy red when he drank too much, and his voice was gravelly. There was nothing particularly striking about his appearance.

"Daniel! Can't you see I'm busy! Stop talking!" Cranitus turned to strike the boy but found that he, too, was staring out at the woman in the garden. "Daniel! I could beat you! Stop daydreaming and hurry! We're leaving."

Joachim was passing through the corridor as Cranitus was leaving. "Ah! Good Cranitus, you hard worker! Always staying late with business, are you? Your wife must adore you for your devotedness!" Joachim slapped the old man hard on the back. He looked at Daniel. "Is that you, Daniel? I almost reached down to tousle your hair! When did you shoot up like a weed? Cranitus, I always knew that scrawny little thing you had was a promising one!"

Cranitus sneered at Daniel and nodded to Joachim. "I do what I can, Joachim. Have a good day," came the terse reply. He marched out the front door and turned to follow the side of the house to where the garden wall began. It was high and covered with vines. Great trees hung their arms of full branches over the side. Tendrils from the flowered branches dipped to the ground, spotting the dusty road with delicate colors of red, pink, and white. The outer wall was beautiful enough to imagine the paradise that must be inside.

On turning the corner, Daniel nearly walked straight into another of the elders standing close to the garden wall.

Persivius fell from the stand he had made out of a wooden crate. He stood and began brushing the dust from his knees, too shocked to reply immediately. Once he had regained composure, he looked up and recognized Daniel. "Cranitus! What servants do you have?"

"Persivius forgive me, good friend. My boy Daniel here is slow." Cranitus glanced down at the stool that Persivius had fallen from. "What are you still here for?"

Persivius also looked down at the stool as if it were a foreign object he had never laid eyes on before. "I lost the cap to my scroll, but must be on my way now. Have a good day." Without looking at them, Persivius began walking toward the litter that waited for him on the other side of the walk.

"He seemed ill," said Cranitus as he watched him leave.

"Maybe it was something he ate," Daniel responded.

This earned him a slap on the back of his neck. "Hush, Daniel! Can't you see I wasn't talking to you?"

"It's going to be a long day," thought Daniel. He fell into step behind his master as they made their way down the road toward his house.

☙

That night Cranitus was surprised to see that most of the people he had had business with that morning were at the wedding feast. Joachim and Persivius were present, mingling among the guests. Cranitus scoffed at the happiness of the feast. He felt suffocated by the density of people in the room. Complaining of a headache, he excused himself. Before moving out to the coolness of the garden, he grabbed a glass of wine.

The steady breeze moved the clouds, causing shadows and light to come in patches across the garden. Cranitus glanced up at the moon, sipping his wine. Suddenly he realized he wasn't alone. He turned and saw Persivius at the other end of the garden. He was walking toward the house. "Persivius!" called out Cranitus. "This is the second time today I see you lurking around gardens. Are you studying the growth patterns of oak trees?" Persivius came within the ring of luminosity that emanated from within the house. In the dim light, his face looked gaunter than normal. His expression was pained. "Cranitus," he said gruffly, "you have always understood me. I feel I can speak openly with you." Cranitus nodded and took his friend by the arm, leading him to the chairs set in the garden.

Once seated, Persivius began, "For eighteen years now I have served Joachim. I have always been loyal to him and he has never had the compassion for me that I deserve. And now, since he married that wife of his four years ago, he has not stopped acting like a young boy in love. It is distracting from his work and burns me to my core. I am filled with envy for the love he has that I have been deprived of."

Cranitus listened in silence, his brows knitted. He nodded in understanding. "Persivius, these things you speak are truth. I have seen it myself. That wife of his is a rare beauty…" he stopped and looked at Persivius. Their eyes met and their glances hardened.

"What is there to do?" Cranitus whispered.

Persivius stood and began pacing back and forth with agitation. "Joachim is leaving in two days for another trip. He will leave me in charge of the household once again." Cranitus stood as well. Persivius continued, "In three days, meet me at noon in his garden. Then we will both get what we deserve." Cranitus nodded his bald head and threw back the dregs of his wine.

75

Persivius disappeared back into the darkness of the garden. His friend watched for a while, then, shivering, he went back to tell his wife they were leaving early.

☙

Three days later, the evening sun set in an array of brilliant red and orange. The courthouse elders were rolling away the last scrolls of the day, eager to return to their homes and enjoy supper with their families. The great wooden door that led from the street into the courtroom suddenly crashed open as an elder barged in yelling, "Adultery!" Every head snapped up to see Cranitus with one hand on the door and the other holding a woman by the scruff of her clothing. Her hair was disheveled and fell in heaps about her face. One of the elders called out to Cranitus, "What drunken state are you in now, old man? What poor beggar do you have there?" Cranitus yanked the woman from her knees and pulled the hair from her face. "Susanna! Wife of Joachim!" Susanna looked about her in confused silence. She was covered in dust and bleeding at the lip from the nasty fall she had taken as Cranitus had roughly dragged her through the streets. The entire way, she had followed in silence, gritting her teeth against his foul words and threats.

"She is being tried for adultery, I say! Bring out the priests! Let them hear it from my own lips!" The group gathered in the courtroom stared in disbelief at Susanna. Some scowled at Cranitus for making such a presumption. He only looked wildly about in his half-drunken state. "Bring the priests here, I say, and I will tell them of how she tried to seduce me!"

"Seduce you? The wife of Joachim, more pure than a newborn lamb, was trying to seduce you, Cranitus, an old man?" Cranitus turned around to face Shedrach. As he turned, he twisted the collar of Susanna's tunic. She gasped for breath. Shedrach, the high priest, reached forward and pulled Susanna's tunic from Cranitus' grasp. She half sat, half laid on the floor, still struggling to breathe. She was barely able to listen to what was going on around her, too dazed to respond.

Just then Persivius sauntered into the courtroom. "It's true; I witnessed it myself. I am here to testify."

"What? You, too, Persivius?" Shedrach said in disgust. Looking down at a confused and ashamed Susanna, Shedrach called for maids to come help her. When they had come, he turned to the two old men who were watching the women. "You two." They looked up. "Come tomorrow morning, when you are more sober, and we will proceed." With that he left, telling the maids to escort Susanna to a room where she could stay until the morning. Joachim was summoned from the port he had gone to. Fortunately, he hadn't set sail due to bad weather.

As the sun declined behind the horizon and gave way to the starry night, Susanna's prayer ascended in fervor. "Lord of Hosts, you know all things and know that those wicked men will accuse me falsely and bring my husband to shame. I beg you, Lord, spare us from this injustice!" The moon that she looked up at gave her no answer. The vast darkness only increased her sense of abandonment and loneliness.

Joachim arrived in the morning, flushed and shouting at those who were impeding him from going to his wife. "I will not believe it!" he ranted. "Bring me to my innocent wife!" Instead, he and the family and friends he brought with him were led to the side of the courtroom where they were instructed to remain silent. They stood in their forlorn lot, weeping quietly, for never could they imagine such an abomination to be blamed on Susanna.

Persivius and Cranitus were seated in the front, their heads down and eyes averted. They looked up only when Susanna was escorted in with her face veiled. She was seated in the midst of the courtroom. The two elders stood and walked over to her. Her veil trembled. Cranitus reached forward and tugged it off. Her pitiful eyes avoided his gaze and searched among the people for her husband. Her eyes filled with tears when she saw him, but she lifted her head in noble character, ready to defend her innocence. She lifted her tear-filled eyes to heaven and whispered in her heart a prayer of wholehearted trust.

Shedrach came in, called the case, and sat down to listen. Susanna cringed when Cranitus and Persivius laid their hands on her head. Persivius began, "As we were walking in the garden alone, this woman entered with two girls and shut the doors of the garden, dismissing the girls. A young man, hidden in a bush, came out and laid with her." He broke off at the gasp that came from the people. Cranitus picked up. "We saw them lying together," he shouted at the disbelieving faces. "But the man we could not hold, for he was stronger than we; he opened the door and ran off. Then we seized this one and asked who the young man was, but she refused to answer." Cranitus had to shout these words over the uproar that had ensued. Spittle flew from his mouth as he hollered, "We testify to this!" Persivius nodded and said as well, "We testify."

Shedrach stood, shaking his head sadly. "This is a sorry accusation brought against someone we thought to be so noble and pure." A woman shouted out from the crowd, "It cannot be true!" Another followed suit, "Re-examine the accusers!" Shedrach looked out upon them sorrowfully and shook his head. "Because these two men are elders and judges, we must take them at their word. It is not in our law to question two judges against one woman." The cries grew. Joachim was horror-struck. He opened and closed his mouth in silent denial. Shedrach couldn't bear to look up when he said, "I sentence Susanna to death."

Susanna stood at once, breaking away from the two men who still had their hands on her. She knelt on the floor and cried aloud, "O eternal God, you know what is hidden and are aware of all things before they come to be; you know that they have testified falsely against me." The entire courtroom fell silent at her words. They rang through the open room. Looking to her husband, and then to heaven, tears began to flow as she pleaded, "Here I am about to die, though I have done none of the things these wicked men have charged me." She fell forward, prostrating herself on the floor, her shoulders heaving as she wept. The mob of wailing women and furious men fell silent with pity. Only Susanna's cries were heard. Joachim whimpered as he joined in her tears. The awful silence enveloped all as they looked accusingly at Shedrach and the two men. "Do something!" they all seemed to say.

Shedrach broke the spell and called for the executioner. He came forward to carry her out to be stoned. Before he reached her, a voice was heard over the wailing that had erupted again. "Wait! I will have no part in this!" Daniel pushed his way forward from the back of the room where he had been told to wait until Cranitus was finished. "I will have no part in the death of this woman!"

He came to the center of the courtroom, where Cranitus was glaring dangerously at him. "Boy, shut up." Instead of being quiet, Daniel went to the chair and stood on it. The people shouted, "What is this about? What do you have to say?" Daniel continued, accusing the accusers, "Are you such fools O Israelites! To condemn a woman of Israel," he turned toward Shedrach, "without examination and without clear evidence?" The wailing abated as he continued. "Let me question these elders, and I will prove they have testified falsely!"

Shedrach gazed at the young man with a white, drawn face. Once again, he found it impossible to look about at the people. They only shouted out, "Who is this young boy come to judge? Let him prove his point or else be sentenced with the woman for his impudence." With hands clasping the back of his chair, Shedrach spoke. "You all know the Law does not permit the re-examination of the elders," he said. The mob's anger increased. "However!" he shouted above them, "however…" They began to grow quiet. "It also is written that if another noble man, unre-lated to the accused, should step forward in defense, he may do so." Everyone turned to Daniel. Shedrach spoke again. "You may proceed."

Daniel turned then to the elders and spoke. "Come, sit and inform us, since God has given you the prestige of old age." They looked at one another in alarm at the turn their plot had taken. Persivius calmly stepped forward. "I will testify to this boy." Cranitus also stepped forward. Daniel turned to him. "No, I will question you both separately. Someone take him outside while I proceed." Throwing threatening glances at Daniel, Cranitus was led out while Persivius took the seat Daniel had gotten down from. The people moved in closer around the two, forming a tight circle, while Susanna was still held by the executioner, who also leaned in to hear this audacious young man.

Daniel paced in front of Persivius, walking behind him and back again. Persivius remained still, staring straight ahead. Finally Daniel stopped in front of him and, pointing his finger at him, exclaimed, "How you have grown evil with age! Now have your past sins come to term. Now then, if you were a witness, tell me under what tree you saw them together." Without flinching, Persivius answered, "A mastic tree. They were under a mastic tree." The crowd looked to one another and whispers filled the air. Daniel turned to them and shouted, "Your fine lie has cost you your head! The angel of God shall receive the sentence from him and split you in two!"

Persivius had gone white at Daniel's words. The young man seemed not to notice as he called for Cranitus and made Persivius stand to the side. As soon as the other old man was seated, Daniel leaned into his face and said, "Offspring of Canaan, not of Judah, beauty has seduced you and lust has subverted your conscience." Cranitus was staring only at Susanna. Hatred flamed in his eyes. Susanna kept her eyes averted. She glanced up only to look at her husband, whose eyes never left her. Daniel stepped back from Cranitus and addressed those assembled. "This is how he acted with the daughters of Judah, and in their fear they yielded to him." The crowd drew back with a disgusted gasp. Daniel pointed to Susanna. "But a daughter of Israel did not tolerate your wickedness. Now then, tell me under what tree you surprised them together."

Everyone stepped in closer to hear his reply. Cranitus had looked up in alarm at the command. He searched the faces surrounding him, looking for evidence as to what Persivius might have said. The array of hard and curious faces betrayed nothing. He began to sputter. "Uh, und-, under a, uh. The t-t-tree I saw them under... Well, an oak. I saw them under an oak tree together," he stated at last with an emphatic nod of his bald head. The crowd gasped in one synonymous breath, holding it in silence. Cranitus stood up and screeched, "An oak tree! Persivius doesn't know which tree is which. His eyes are bad!" One of Susanna's relatives shouted out, "Joachim's garden has no oaks!" Cranitus turned where he stood, trying to find a sympathetic face. "What do trees tell you? I saw them. I saw them I say!" But it was too late. Daniel came up to him and laid his hands on his head. "Your fine lie has cost you your head! The angel of God shall receive the sentence from him and split you in two!"

Someone brought Persivius forward, and the two men were led out of the courtroom while the entire crowd filed out behind them. Joachim and Susanna were left alone. She was sitting on the floor where the executioner had left her. Joachim stood looking down at her upturned face. He held out his hand. She grasped it and stood. He led her over to the court bench and sat down with her there. Taking her hand into his he said, "Do you want to go home?" She shook her head. "What do you want then?" Lowering her head, she asked quietly, "Do you believe me?" Joachim didn't hesitate to answer. "Yes, I do." Susanna looked up, the lines of strain still creasing her face. Joachim took the end of his cloak and wiped away the blood that was on her cut lip. "But tell me what happened so we can get it straight."

Susanna nodded and stood. "Yesterday afternoon, the day after you left, I went to the garden to bathe, as I sometimes do on hot days." Joachim nodded. "I dismissed the maids, asking them to lock the gate, and I would find them when I finished.

"After they left, I sat by the water, looking in at it and enjoying my solitude when a face appeared opposite me. I looked up into the face of Cranitus. He was standing there smiling. I was startled and asked who had let him in. He didn't answer but came around the pond toward me. I stood my ground and demanded that he tell me how he had entered. When I saw him coming still closer, I tried to back up but bumped into Persivius. Before I could scream, he had his hand over my mouth.

"I was helpless after that. They told me to give in to their desires or else face the end of an adulterer." Susanna stopped

82

before her husband. "Joachim, I struggled to free myself. Cranitus told Persivius to allow me to speak. In my heart, I prayed to God, 'Lord, I am trapped. But I will not give in to the desires of men but rather stand before your laws, for you know all things.' As soon as he uncovered my mouth, I screamed.

"That was when the servants came running in through the side gate. Imagine the scene they came upon! Those two evil men had planned their scheme well."

Joachim put his hand up. "Enough. You have told me enough, and I still believe you. I never once doubted your innocence. You are my wife and I know you as well as I know myself. Now that you have told me the truth, we can put this all behind us." He stood, smiled at her, and said, "Come now; our God has saved us both today. He has saved you from death and me from losing my lovely young wife." Susanna smiled in return.

The New Testament

The Syropheonician Woman

"Look to God that you may be radiant with joy and your faces may not blush with shame. In my misfortune I called, the Lord heard, and saved me from all distress."

PSALM 34:6-7

I never left your side. For hours I would lie on a mat beside you, waking up to put cold rags on your forehead, or even just to sing to you. I prayed much, too. I prayed when you would toss and turn, moaning in fits of pain and delirium. I prayed for Yahweh to save my only girl."

Abigail sat up in her bed. "Yes, I remember! I mean, I don't remember all the prayers, but I remember hearing you pray once. I woke up, but I kept my eyes closed."

Sheila crossed her arms. "So you were pretending to be sick?"

Abigail grabbed her mother's arm. "No, Mom! I just heard you that one time. I'll tell you what you said. You prayed, 'Yahweh, look kindly on your people. We are sinful and full of error, but we need you. Send someone to heal my daughter. Send Jesus of Nazareth, the healer. But if it be your will, Lord, then please take my daughter to Abraham's bosom when she dies. Amen.'"

Sheila nodded at her daughter. She looked around her at the room that was the same she had spent so many hours of wondering, waiting, and suffering. How many tears she had wept at this very spot! How many prayers she had prayed! Sheila remembered the twinge of despair that threatened to overwhelm her at each stage of Abigail's sickness.

"Mom, Dad told me once that there were three days that you didn't eat anything. Is that true?" Abigail's hazel eyes, so much like her father's, looked at her mother with concern. Sheila nodded, her heart once again feeling the pain she felt then. "I was dying with you."

Abigail sat up again. "Well, come on. Tell me about how I was cured! I didn't die; tell me how again!"

Smiling, Sheila told Abigail to lie back down for bed and set aside the tunic she was mending.

"You had gone from bad to worse. I continued to pray, but my prayer of petition turned to one of acceptance at your inevitable death. There was one day in which you seemed to have reached a peak. You weren't getting better, but neither were you getting worse. One of our neighbors came bursting into the room. 'Sheila! Yahweh has heard your prayers! Jesus of Nazareth is in Tyre, and he is staying at my brother's house!' My heart nearly stopped. Your father was there and asked if they could bring the healer here to the house. The neighbor said no because he didn't want people knowing that he was in the area.

"So then we discussed taking you there, but you were in too bad a condition and we were afraid you wouldn't make it if we moved you. So in the end, I decided that I would have to go. It was the last resort. I was afraid of being turned away. I was afraid he wouldn't have the power to heal you, but deep down, I hoped for a miracle.

"It took some persuading to get our neighbor to agree to take us. You see, she forgot to say that she wasn't supposed to tell us whom her brother was hosting. We just told her to tell you no, and that changed her mind. That very afternoon, she led me to her brother's house and left me at the doorstep."

Abigail sat up from bed. "I can't believe she just left you there. Weren't you afraid?"

"Lie back down. No, I wasn't afraid. Someday when you are a mother, you will learn what it is to see your child dying. There is nothing stronger than the love a mother can have for her children. They are her own flesh and blood. The bonds of love can lead one to do the most courageous acts, even when one feels no end to the fear.

"It was courage, my daughter. Courage gave me the strength to start out through the town toward the house where Jesus was. I stood at the front door, pushing away the reality that threatened to choke me. I had never seen the man. I didn't know if he would take kindly to me, a woman, and a Syropheonician at that! He was a Jew, from Galilee. I was beginning to wonder where my courage had gone when the door opened. I hadn't knocked. I had been standing there wondering what I was going to say. The man standing before me growled down his crooked nose. Two bushy black eyebrows that sat like wool on his forehead shadowed his eyes. His beard was just as fierce and unruly. I almost sank into the ground.

"'What do you want?' he growled at me. Before I could answer, a younger man came up behind. 'Peter, do you really think the master would tell you to open the door like that for a beggar?

She's ready to cry. Look at her.' The fearsome man's expression didn't change, but he did move away from the door. He revealed the inside of a dark but well-kept home. The young man who had pleaded on my behalf motioned for me to enter. I did, and I saw that to the right of the door was another man. He was standing with the owner of the house. They were bent over an unfolded scroll, studying it intensely. I stood just beyond his line of vision, waiting, trying to summons courage. I moved forward and cleared my throat. He looked up."

"This is my favorite part!" Abigail interrupted. "I remember this part for sure. You always say that his eyes were so intense. There was nothing particular about their color. They were brown, like everyone's, but there was something different, something deeper about them."

Sheila smiled but said, "That's right, but we will have to finish tomorrow. It is past your bedtime already and this story isn't putting you to sleep but making you more awake!"

Abigail laid back again. "No! I promise I won't interrupt anymore. Please, finish."

ↃↃ

"Alright, where was I? Right, I had just entered the house. I was keenly aware of my poverty. I had nothing to bargain for his grace but my empty hands. He looked up and I sank to my knees. 'Lord, I know I am only a Greek, and you are a Jew, but, if you will, you can cure my daughter. She is possessed by a demon and gravely ill. She will die if you don't come. Please.' I whispered the last word. It came from the depth of my heart, but I never took my eyes from his face. He had turned when I went to my knees and was studying the scroll before him. 'Let the children be fed first.' He said this slowly and then turned his gaze toward me. His eyes almost held a challenge as he said, 'It is not right to take the food from the children to give to the dogs.'

"My spirit sank through the floor. I remained kneeling, but inside, I was dead. He wasn't going to help me. I am Greek, unclean to the Jews. He kept looking at me with the same challenge in his face. It wasn't harsh, but almost encouraging. I closed my eyes and at that moment, I thought of you, Abigail. In my mind I saw you as you used to be, healthy and loving. Then I saw you struggling for life on your deathbed.

"No. The thought slammed through my mind. I opened my eyes and returned the healer's gaze. 'Lord...' My voice cracked, but I continued. 'Even the dogs are given the scraps from the table.'

"It seems odd, Abigail, but as I knelt there, I almost felt as though this rabbi were encouraging me to persist. He was encouraging me by his gaze but also by his nearness. I waited for what felt like an eternity. I waited for him to speak. I couldn't look at him, though; I was afraid of reading the answer in his eyes. So I waited, kneeling before him, with the three other men frozen in the room, watching, waiting as well. Then Jesus bent down. I had been kneeling with my hands clasped in front of me. He bent down and grasped my arms. He pulled me up until I was standing. I looked at him and his eyes had changed from challenging to peaceful. They were radiant. He whispered to me. 'Your child is well. Your faith has saved her. Go now and be with her.'"

Abigail sat up again. "What did you say?"

"I didn't say a thing. I couldn't. He led me silently to the door and I stood at the opening for a few moments. The young man who had helped me in the beginning touched my shoulder. I jumped. 'Woman, I think you better go to your daughter now.'

"I looked at him and nodded, then fled, running to see you. I arrived to the house to see your father outside, weeping. 'No!' I thought. 'She has to be alive! She can't be dead. He said… he said…' I ran up to your father. He looked at me and choked out, 'She's well!' I entered the house and saw you sleeping peacefully. There was no sign of fever. You had the color of life in your cheeks. You were healed.

"That is when our neighbor proceeded to tell the whole story. About twenty minutes earlier you had woken up and asked for something to eat. They fed you and you fell back to sleep. Your father was so overcome that he had gone out to cry. You were dying, Abigail. You wouldn't be here if it weren't for Jesus of Nazareth."

"Mom, don't start crying now. You know I also wouldn't be here if you hadn't done what you did. You saved my life as well."

Sheila wasn't listening; she was still caught up in her memory. "I don't know what it was," she mused aloud. "It was something supernatural that compelled me to believe I could convince him to heal you. I really believed that."

Abigail yawned. "I'm glad you believed, Mom. Thank you for telling me the story again!" Sheila tucked Abigail in for the night, then leaned over and blew out the candle.

The Widow of Nain

"The spirit of the Lord God is upon me, because the Lord has anointed me; He has sent me to bring glad tidings to the lowly, to heal the brokenhearted... to give them oil of gladness in place of mourning, a glorious mantle instead of a listless spirit."

Isaiah 61:1,3

Michaela, I know it is difficult to answer this question so close after his death, but it has to be asked. What are you going to do now? ... Michaela, are you listening?"

The words seemed to be coming to her as though from the inside of a cave, echoing through her mind. His death. Phillip, her son, was dead. Was it only three days ago that he had complained of stomach pains? The fever was so high. He had tossed and turned for hours, moaning. It all happened so fast, and now... What was she going to do?

"I don't know. I don't know. God took him away. He will provide," she whispered, looking down at her weathered hands. Her neighbor sat down next to her at the table and poured hot water into her cup. The steam swirled through the air, floating away into nothing. The three women watched it absentmindedly. Michaela's other neighbor sat down as well and grabbed her open hands that were resting on the table.

"Yes, Michaela, I believe in God's providence, too, but you still have to think about yourself. Andrew has no brothers, and now your only source of income is your weavings." Michaela winced at the callous truth. Nevertheless, her faith answered, "God provided when he took Andrew last year. He will provide again." Too tired to discuss further, Michaela stood and walked into her room. Her neighbors stayed sitting and watched her walk away.

"Poor thing, she hasn't slept in the past four days, ever since he came home ill…" The woman grabbed the cup of hot water to warm her hands. It had cooled, though, and no longer emitted wisps of steam.

"What a life she's had in the past year and a half." They shook their heads sadly.

"And now, if she doesn't do something, she will end up on the streets, begging in the gutters." Michaela's friend sighed deeply at the misfortune that had befallen the little house she sat in.

"Well for now the least we can do is let her rest while we prepare the boy for burial tomorrow afternoon."

"Yes, let's go." They stood from the table where the pot of hot water and herbs sat untouched and left.

☙

Black shawl in place, Michaela closed the door of her home and turned toward the small crowd of loud mourners. It made her stomach clench to hear the exaggerated wailings. She knew that the louder the cries, the less authentic the mourning. Such were the ways of Nain's people, seizing any chance to make a show.

The procession began. Bands of sorrow clenched around her heart as she saw the funeral bier approaching. It was covered in a black cloth that fluttered in the breeze. She could see her son's form through it. Four somber-faced men carried it upon their shoulders. She knew their sadness was genuine. Phillip had many friends who loved him for the wonderful boy he was. He had been so full of life. The procession began to move and Michaela could no longer hold back her tears. For the first time since her son breathed his last, she gave in to a fit of overwhelming grief. Leaning upon her neighbor, she wept through the streets of Nain.

The narrow street Michaela lived on opened into a wider one that led to the main square. The sand-colored buildings stood at lopsided angles and in misshapen forms. A fat and drowsy-looking woman leaned over her balcony, intent on fresh gossip for her morning trip to the well. Across the street from her was a shriveled old man who was so overcome by the mass of people that he shrank even more into his spot on the steps. Men, women, and children crowded the doorways and windows of their houses to see the commotion that was passing. Some joined the procession when they heard who it was to pay their respects. Others joined to be in on the show. The crowd grew larger. Michaela stayed close to her son, taking everything in. The procession moved on.

At last they came to the city gate. It rose above the walls it cut through. The wooden gate creaked as it was slowly swung open. This was the last stretch until they came to the burial site just outside the walls. It was the same spot that Andrew and her father were buried. It seemed only yesterday to Michaela that

she and her husband were carrying a small Phillip through these
gates to bury her father. Her head became dizzy with the memories stirring around in it. The pain of his death would have
been unbearable if it had not been for the comfort her loved
ones gave her. But now, to whom would she turn? There was no
shoulder to cry on this time. Now she would have to face reality
alone. Now she would have to make a different life. Shaking
herself from haunting thoughts of the future, she came back to
her march.

By now the procession flooded the narrow street and the din
was almost unbearable. "If only they would be silent," thought
Michaela. "I don't want all this noise and commotion for Phillip. He never enjoyed large crowds." Her tears began again and
this time she couldn't help the moaning that came from within.
At least her cries drowned out the others. "Silence. All I want is
silence." The thought resounded through her empty heart. "I need
to be alone. I need to think. I need…"

"Silence." Michaela wasn't sure if she had said it out loud or if
someone else had.

"Silence." This time she heard a man's distinctive voice carrying through the crowd. She looked around to see who had said
it. A man was standing at the city's gates, flanked by a group of
followers. Three men, two older and one younger, were breaking
through the crowd, clearing a path for their master. He had been
the one to speak. Though he had only spoken one word, his firm
voice had reached each person.

"Silence." He said it again, this time with more force, though
not fiercely. The crowd seemed to listen. The clamor died down
to murmurs and faded away to nothing. The crowd was still,
and there was silence. Everyone turned to the man. He stood
still, only his head moving slowly, spanning the crowd. His eyes

seemed to take in the entire scene at once. The horde of onlookers encircled the cluster of the bereaved. His eyes understood the situation and he centered on Michaela. She saw his eyes cut through the throng of people and rest on her. His concentrated gaze seemed to soften. She was reminded of her father.

Is that why his face seemed familiar? She couldn't figure it out. There was something more to it than a resemblance. She had seen it before. Like a flash, she was brought back to the previous year, when she had gone on pilgrimage to Jerusalem.

⚘

"Mother, it is so noisy here! I thought the temple was only for those to offer sacrifice and worship. Who are all these people?"

"They're the money changers, Phillip."

Michaela looked down at the concern on her son's face. He had the same crease in his forehead as his father had. They were so much alike… Michaela sighed. Andrew had been dead only a few months, and it already felt like years. "Still," she thought to herself, "God has been so good to have left me with a boy that takes such good care of me."

"Phillip, don't worry about others. You should only be concerned with where you stand before God. Come on now, we only have to put our contribution in the treasury and then we can start back to Nain." Phillip seemed distracted from his previous worry and took up a new one. "Mother, we have only two coins left. What will we give?"

"We will give to Yahweh as much as he has given to us," his mother stated confidently.

"And then?" he persisted.

"And then he will provide."

They entered the treasury portico and squeezed around the giant pillars and large, flowing tunics of the rich. They were loudly counting out their coins as they dropped them into the box in the middle of the room. Michaela left Phillip next to a pillar and skirted around the fire pots that hung low from the ceiling. She pushed in behind an enormous woman who smelled of oils and incense, and pulled out her leather pouch. Two copper coins slipped out and clinked into her palm. She fisted her hand, lifted it toward the sanctuary and released the coins without a moment's hesitation. Glancing up, she spotted a man looking at her from across the hall. He had been watching her, she could tell. For a moment, she couldn't hear the people around her. Then the oily woman flung her head-wrap over her shoulder and into Michaela's face. By the time she had gotten the wooly cloth out of her eyes, the man was gone. She turned and walked back to her son, and, taking him by the hand, left the temple area.

"Mother, why are you so silent?" Phillip had been skipping alongside; chatting away about the cousins he had seen on their annual pilgrimage. Michaela didn't notice that her mind had wandered.

"What's that? Nothing. I was just remembering something." Michaela was remembering the man at the temple. What was it about his face?

C3

That's the face! He is the one who was at the temple. The connection rang through Michaela's head. For some reason, she felt oddly consoled at his presence. *I don't understand. I've never spoken to him. Why do I feel so close to him?* she thought to herself.

Just as someone was about to ask what the man was doing, he

stepped forward. He advanced steadily through the people and came up next to the bier, where she stood.

"Your son?" he asked quietly.

"My only son," she whispered.

"Yes, your only son."

He said these words with a distant look in his eyes, as if recalling a remote memory. His eyes seemed almost to fill with tears, and he raised them upward. His lips were moving, as in prayer. Again, she was reminded of her father. It only made her hurt deeper.

"Woman," he said, breaking through her wonderings, "do not weep any longer." Michaela looked at him, confused. He stepped closer to the coffin and, lifting the black cloth, spoke. "Young man, I tell you, arise!"

Before a thought could cross her mind, Michaela's son sat up. The four men carrying the bier nearly dropped it in their surprise. Phillip sat on the floor speaking in confused words. His shroud lay in heaps about him and his face was white as chalk. He looked about, startled at the crowd. There was silence everywhere except for his stammering. The hundreds of people crammed in the street were staring dumbly at the boy. Each person seemed to be holding his breath, waiting for the ghost to disappear. In his span of the crowd, he turned toward his mother. His search stopped on her astonished face. Recognition sprang to his eyes, then concern. "Mother!" he cried. "Why are you weeping?" He leapt up and ran to her, color flooding his features once again.

A wave of astonished murmurs rippled through the crowd, and then an explosion of noise as people began pressing forward. They were shouting, "God has visited his people!" and, "Who is this great prophet that has risen among us?" They pressed in to touch Phillip and the miracle worker. The three men accompanying him were pushing the crowd off, yelling at them to keep their distance. The man didn't appear agitated, though; he calmly observed the people in their frenzy. Michaela still stood with her son, off to the side, almost forgotten. She saw the man's gaze cut through the crowd once again. She smiled at him through her tears of joy. He nodded and followed his disciples, who were pressing him to leave. Michaela's heart dropped when she saw him turn and walk through the crowd. Amazingly, they parted to let him pass. They were afraid as he walked by with as much authority as a king.

"Mother, where is he going?" Phillip asked. "I had the strangest dream and he was in it." Michaela turned to look at her beloved son. He was healthier than he had ever been. "Don't worry, son, I don't think we have seen the last of him." She smiled reassuringly at him. He grinned back and held out his arm. "Come on, then; let's go home!"

The crowd was already dispersing. Only small pockets seemed to recall that Phillip was a living miracle. They approached him and his mother as they made their way home. They all stared in astonishment as he conversed and laughed with them, teasing the little children. Michaela couldn't take her eyes off of him. It was as if it were the day he had been born. It was as if he had been born again.

The Sinful Woman

> *"Has anyone hoped in the Lord and been disappointed? Has anyone persevered in his fear and been forsaken? Has anyone called upon him and been rebuffed? Compassionate and merciful is the Lord; he forgives sins, he saves in time of trouble."*
>
> SIRACH 2:10-11

But what is this prophet's name? And where does he come from? You can't be too careful about false prophets. You know, my brother-in-law was swindled into believing the Messiah was coming. He thought it was at midnight in Judea on his son's wedding day. You should have seen the fool he made of himself. He was stripped down to his under-tunic with his beard shorn clean off. He had placed all his possessions in the main hall to keep them safe once the Messiah took him away. We howled for days over it. When no one came after two hours, he became so enraged he sent everyone home three days early!"

Dinah's eyes widened to the size of figs. "Rachel, it's blasphemous to talk about the Messiah like that." Rachel crossed her arms and pointed her nose in the air. "Dinah, he's not here, is he? Besides, it was my brother-in-law who did it, not me. I warned my sister from the beginning not to let Father wed her to that buffoon. She never listened to me, though, and now she's paid for it." She shrugged at the memory and turned to Dinah. "Anyway, Dinah, you never answered my question. Tell me what the Sanhedrin are doing about this false prophet."

Dinah held up her hands. "No, Rachel, I didn't say he was false. This one is different. My husband's cousin's neighbor has heard him preach and she said she's never seen someone speak with so much authority." Her gestures wildly displayed the origins of her knowledge, working out the intricate lineage of the news. "She was at the Mount of Olivet last week and said that he spoke with so much clarity and genuine concern. Then he began to work miracles and heal people with leprosy and everything!"

"Leprosy? Is that Tiloma who told you that?" Rachel's face contorted as she looked down her nose at Dinah.

"Yes," Dinah answered, crossing her arms.

"Well, no wonder. I wouldn't trust that source with my own child. She has a reputation for weaving tales more elaborate than the baskets she sells, if you ask me." Dinah scoffed at Rachel. "Well, if you don't trust Tiloma, maybe Jeruzabel can convince you. She was there before this prophet was even known. She was present when John baptized him in the Jordan."

"Mhmm," said Rachel, now crossing her arms. "Dinah, are you so naïve? Anyone who has had anything to do with that crazy locust-eating savage is not at all reliable. That prophet, if John baptized him, has lost all, if there ever was any, esteem that I held for him as a man of God. Because it is obvious that he is not."

"But you should see Tiloma. She's a different person after hearing him. Now she's one of the most pious women I know."

"Is that right?" Rachel asked with raised eyebrows.

"Besides you, of course."

"Why, thank you, Dinah. You're a true friend. But as for that prophet, I'm still not sure about him. I've heard he has eaten with tax collectors. That sounds a little shady to me. What was his name again?"

Dinah breathed in deeply. "Jesus of Nazareth."

Rachel laughed out loud. "Nazareth? Does anything good ever come out of –"

"Shhhh! Here comes the mistress."

Peering out from the niche in the stone corridor, the two maidservants saw their mistress gliding down the breezy hall. They lowered their eyes in deference.

Her cool blue eyes scanned their forms as she walked by. An accountant fluttered around her arm, chattering off numbers and dates. Samara seemed not to hear him as she kept walking toward the garden.

"Those eyes!" Rachel seethed in contempt. "Where does she get those eyes? They're blue like the sky. You don't see that color from anywhere around here. They belong to a possessed person."

Dinah leveled Rachel with a look. "Rachel, don't exaggerate. You know her father was a mercenary, traveling around from this battle to that. It's obvious he picked up more than just spoils in his campaigns…" She kept gazing down the hall where Samara had gone.

Rachel snapped into Dinah's musings. "I still don't like working for a foreigner. I just have a bad feeling about her. And Dinah, you know my intuitions are almost always right. Besides, growing up in such an unstable and cruel environment… always surrounded by men… shifting from one battlefield to the next… it has to have its effects on a girl." Dinah nodded thoughtfully while Rachel continued to pour out her poisonous thoughts. "Everyone knows she was married to the master only as a cover for her shameful state. And what would one expect? Living among only men, and in such conditions? Well, if no one knew before, they have only to look at her sons now. They have their mother's eyes, but they certainly have their fathers' looks, and both different completely." Dinah gave a sharp look to Rachel, who only shrugged and added, "The proof is there for all to see. But what we don't know is who it was. Although I have my speculations…"

Dinah lifted her hand and turned her head. "Stop there! Say what you want; she has never given us any grief. Even if her look does pierce right through you, there is no proof to those tales."

"Fine, be that way," Rachel huffed. "But it seems she inherited more than just blue eyes from her mother – a reputation to match as well!" She nodded down the hall to emphasize her point. Dinah continued to scold her, glancing around nervously, afraid someone might be listening. Rachel just kept complaining. "Those eyes! I wonder if she ever even blinks…."

The quiet conversation drifted down the hall as the servants moved away from their "news niche."

☙

Samara had dismissed the tiresome little man and was now seated upon the garden bench, staring at the sky. One lonely cloud flitted across the blue expanse. "Poppy, if the sky is so big, why don't we fall into it?" Samara remembered asking her father as a child. His answer came to her every time she looked up.

"Little girl, why do you ask such silly questions? The sky is that big and we are just insects here, lost in the land we live. That's the only answer I know." He told her to go play with the other little girls and left.

"Lost in the land we live." Samara sighed to herself but then straightened up when she heard the shrill voices of her two sons chanting their Hebrew recitations from the other side of the garden. She smiled. They were looking forward to having one of their friends over the next day. It was a task to keep them still for even one moment.

Samara stood up from the bench and went over to where she could watch them without their becoming distracted. She gazed out at their faces, so different, like their personalities.

"Lost in the land we live." A familiar melancholy settled upon her chest. *If only I could find a friend to brighten my day as my boys do,* she thought. *A friend. How ridiculous! Who would be a friend to a sinner?*

☙

"Simon, excellent reflection on Scripture today. You make coming to the synagogue enjoyable." The rotund middle-aged man rubbed his belly with one hand as he spoke. With the other, he fixed the phylacteries that were forever crooked on his small, bald head.

Simon gave a big, fake smile. "Why thank you, Tereth! If you'd like to hear more, I've been invited by the high priest to preach at the temple next Sabbath."

"What an honor!" Tereth beamed. "Thank you for the invitation. I will surely be there, and I'll bring my kinsmen as well." Simon stopped listening; he was distracted by something green caught in between Tereth's front teeth. Tereth didn't notice but continued to praise Simon. "They surely will be impressed by the friends I have! You are nearly as good a preacher as that prophet from Nazareth!"

Simon drew closer to Tereth. "Who's that?"

"I think his name is Jesus, from Nazareth in Galilee. He has been quite popular lately, though no one from his town seems to favor him. They drove him out of their synagogue last month! Other than that incident, though, he has quite a way with crowds. I think it is because of his healing powers. Some people call him a prophet."

"Healing powers?" Simon leaned forward intently to make sure Tereth wasn't spinning another tale. He could be worse than a woman at a well sometimes. The squat man only nodded. "Yes, in fact he was in Judea, across the Jordan, just last week. You were there, too, weren't you? I'm surprised you didn't hear of him."

Simon stared blankly at Tereth, seeing into the past week, remembering the Nazarene's words addressed to the group of Pharisees that had cornered him. "Because of the hardness of your hearts, Moses permitted divorce. But from the beginning, 'God created them male and female. For this reason a man shall leave his father and mother and be joined to his wife, and they shall become one flesh.' So they are no longer two, but one. Therefore, what God has joined together, no human being must separate." From his place on the outskirts of the crowd, Simon had avoided looking at the preacher. However, this didn't stop the words from reaching him.

"Simon?" Tereth was waving his plump hand in front of his face.

Simon pulled back and began to comb his fingers through his beard. "Hmmm." While examining the end of his tassel, he asked, "Where is the preacher now?"

"He's here in Jerusalem. My wife went out to hear him at the Mount of Olivet this past week. She's won over, but she can be rather fanatic. Speaking of which, I better get going. If I leave her alone too long, she tries becoming the master of the household, ordering my servants around and all. You should see it! What I wouldn't give to be a bachelor like you, Simon."

"Yes, well, until next week then." Simon hadn't heard anything after "Jerusalem." The two men gave hearty slaps on the back to each other and parted.

Simon then began to slowly make his way through Jerusalem's crowded, confusing streets. The back ways he took were dark and close. He wandered past stinking gutters and piles of rotting wood. Just as he was about to cross over onto the high streets, he paused. From underneath the shadow of a toppled archway, he gazed out onto the bright square. Asian rug-and-spice sellers shouted bargains to those passing by. Barefoot children shrieked in delight as they played tag and stole dates from the fruit stands. He stared out upon the day but saw a different scene in his mind.

℞

The deep blue tent rustled slightly as a cool night's breeze seeped in through the flaps. One of the flaps was undone, and a gust of wind tossed it aside, knocking over a stick propped there. The thud made Simon freeze. He looked down at the sleeping form of his wife to see if she would wake. Lifting her arm, she rubbed her face but continued sleeping. Simon breathed a sigh of relief and then turned to finish bundling together his things. It was a small bundle. A mercenary always travels lightly. Before lifting the flap to leave, he glanced once again upon her. For one moment, he felt a twinge of guilt, but it quickly vanished. He knew he couldn't continue the way they were. Swinging the bundle over his shoulder, he turned and left the tent, leaving behind a few pieces of silver and all his memories of the past four months.

❦

"I wonder what you are thinking of." Simon snapped out of his reverie and looked down to see who had spoken. A small old man sat on a blanket behind the arch and had obviously been watching him for a while.

"Narubi? Is that you?" He bent down to get a better look at his face. Simon recognized the scar that stretched from his left ear to his mouth, the trophy of a knife fight from years before. When he smiled, the scar contracted making it look like he had two mouths. Children were terrified of him. Simon spoke again when the old merchant didn't answer. "I thought you were in Malta until autumn."

Narubi looked up to Simon and answered in his gruff voice, "Yeah, I thought so, too, until a pestilence broke out in the city. I left early because people were dying by the cartload. I wanted to get as far away as possible."

Simon laughed and softly kicked at one of the scrolls Narubi was selling. "You're still the same pagan! Selling scrolls on a Sabbath! You know I ought to turn you in."

"Turn me in to whom? You're the one who makes the prescriptions! Besides, why would you do that to your old friend when he has good news for you?" Narubi shifted his turban so he could see Simon better.

"News?" Simon's eyebrows rose as he drew out the word.

"It's about that Jesus of Nazareth," he said. Simon nodded. Narubi continued, "He'll be outside the temple tomorrow morning. I thought of you as soon as I got that bit of information." He cooed the words, trying to warm Simon up. "I knew you would find him interesting and would perhaps want to become acquainted with such a controversial fellow. Calls himself a prophet, you know." Narubi paused to see if Simon would ask more or pay up. Simon stood where he was, combing his fingers through his beard.

Finally he reached into his tunic and said, "Narubi, good friend, I'm glad you're back!" He flicked his thumb, and a gold coin catapulted into the air. Narubi snatched the glinting coin and hoarded it away into his many folds of rags. "Always here to help," he grumbled, slighted by the small amount. "Anytime, anytime. We're old friends, you know." Simon looked at Narubi, piercing him with a warning look. Narubi smiled and began to chuckle. He bowed in mock respect, and when he looked up, Simon was walking away. Narubi laughed to himself and, pulling his turban down again, resumed his inspection of the people that passed.

As Simon continued his walk home, he reflected on the events of the morning. It wasn't even noon, and already he had heard about that preacher twice. His face flushed. He asked himself, *Who is that preacher that so many are flocking to?* Simon decided he had to meet the man for himself. As soon as he arrived home, he sent his messenger out with a note for Jesus of Nazareth. It was an invitation to feast at the prominent Pharisee's home. While waiting for the response, he sat down to work on his sermon for next week in the temple.

Narubi's eerie face came floating into his mind. He frowned at the memory Narubi had caught onto.... They were young then, years before Simon had become zealous for the Law. He shuddered involuntarily at the memory of the wife he had left behind in Troas. *Wife,* he thought. *I can't even call the pagan ceremony we had a marriage.* The same thoughts and justifications sprang to the fore as always. *After six years, why can't I finally forget? She had never been interested in anything lasting anyway. There were many men there she could still properly marry if she wanted.* Slamming his fist on the table smashed the memory. Simon began writing furiously.

An hour later the messenger returned with the reply. He was coming. Simon smiled to himself. It would be interesting to see who this man really was… surely there was something in his past that could be used against him. Surely there would be some way of discrediting the commotion he was creating among the Jews. That something would have to wait for the next day.

CB

"Excuse me, miss? Would you like to see our finest silks imported from India? Would you like to feel them? There is nothing more brilliant in color or finer in texture this side of the Jordan." Samara ignored the plump man waving materials in her face. It was the best way to get rid of the pesky market flies.

I knew I should have gone the long way, she thought to herself. Just then her son spoke up. "Mama, where are we going?" Nathaniel swung the basket he was carrying back and forth with increasing force.

"Nathaniel, don't swing that so hard. The fruit will fall out and be spoiled." This earned her a pout, which she ignored. "We're going to your Gran's house." The pout turned to a grimace.

"Oh no, please, don't make me go," he whined, dragging his feet. "Why didn't Benjamin have to come instead of me? Now Gran will have me sit and listen to the birds in her garden with her. I hate sitting in the garden. Mama, please, can't I go to Jacob's house? He lives near here."

Samara began her lecture about respecting the elderly. But then a great crowd of people gathered in the square made her forget what she was saying. They were silent, listening to a man. Even Nathaniel sensed something and stopped whining. Samara moved up to the edge of the crowd to see who was speaking. Nathaniel instinctively drew closer to his mother.

"Then to what will I compare the people of this generation? They are like children who sit in the marketplace and call to one another. 'We played the flute for you but you did not dance. We sang a dirge, but you did not weep.'"

Two haggish women in front of Samara began to speak. "Who did you say he is, Matilda?" The second woman answered, "His name is Jesus of Nazareth, a prophet that follows the Baptizer. He supposedly is the one that river frog was announcing."

The other woman broke out into a hoarse guffaw. "Quiet, Helga! He's still speaking." Helga hid her laugh with a forced cough. "I was here when he first came into the marketplace. A messenger from Simon the Pharisee's household came up and invited the prophet for a feast tomorrow. He accepted."

"Hmm, I wonder what those Pharisees are up to now."

"Who knows, probably keeping their eyes open for anyone who might overshadow them. Their worst nightmare is to come in second place on the Sabbath." The woman hacked out another laugh. Her friend turned to her with annoyance now. "Helga, that wasn't even meant to be funny." Helga coughed some more and then asked, "But Matilda, what about this prophet? Why are people flocking to him?"

Matilda shrugged her shoulders. "Because he has powers of some sort. He heals people. Not just any people, though." The wrinkled woman was in her element. Helga was hanging on her every word. Matilda lowered her voice furtively. "He even heals

sinners. Some have even been calling him the friend of sinners."
She whispered the word "friend," savoring the effect. "They aren't
far off, though. One of his followers was a tax collector." Samara
leaned close to hear the last words, which were almost inaudible.

"Ouch! You're stepping on my foot!" Samara jumped back
and apologized to Nathaniel. She looked up to find the whole
crowd had turned to see who had shouted. The Nazarene had
been conversing with one of the men following him. He looked
up to see what the disturbance was. He looked straight at Samara. She froze for half a heartbeat then pulled her veil more
tightly around her face and moved away with Nathaniel in tow.
When she had reached the edge of the square, she turned to have
one last look. *Who is that 'friend of sinners'?* Forgetting about her
husband's mother, Samara turned back toward home.

That night, after kissing her boys good night, she went out to
stroll in the garden. The images from that day tumbled into her
head. The words the Nazarene had said: What did they mean?
The conversation the two women had held. "A friend of sinners…
to Simon's house for a feast…" There was something tugging at
Samara's heart.

"Why would I go there tomorrow? What would that gain
me?" Samara asked the great oak in front of her.

"What could you lose?" it seemed to answer.

For twenty minutes more, she paced from the oak to the
garden wall and back again. Just when she was deciding to stay at
home, little Benjamin came out, dragging a blanket behind him.

"Mama, I can't sleep." He yawned.

"Come here, you can sit with me while I think." Samara
settled on the bench and pulled her son close to her.

"Mama?"

"Yes?"

"Why are you always so sad?"

Samara looked down at her son, who had been watching her think. "Am I sad?"

"Yes, I think it is because you need a friend." He yawned again.

A sword of truth cut down the excuses she had built up with so much care. "Benjamin, I think you're right." Little Benjamin didn't hear her answer. He was sound asleep in his mother's lap.

She continued to gaze down upon her son, wondering at the insight of children. As she ran her fingers through his brown curls, she marveled at his distinct looks. So much like his father. The thought startled her, and she looked up to see if anyone was there. She stood up, scooping Benjamin into her arms and carrying him inside. Even after laying him next to his brother, she stayed watching them as they slept. Brown curls and black hair. At least their eyes were both the vibrant blue of their mother's. Those eyes were closed now, and Samara decided to follow suit, leaving her preoccupations to the side for the moment.

☙

With morning, the worries came back full force. The pit in her stomach grew as she turned down the street where Simon lived. *What makes you think, Samara, that seeing this so-called friend of sinners is going to take away the guilt you feel? Nothing will change. Your children will always be there to remind you, as will your servants. Besides, you know to whose house you are going. You know the trap you are stepping into. Turn around. It's not worth the humiliation.*

Samara once again pushed away the thoughts that threatened to choke off her resolve. *Enough is enough,* she thought. *If I don't take the risk now, I will never forgive myself. This is my last resort.*

So what if it is at Simon's house? He won't speak out for fear of being discovered. After all these years, he still refuses to acknowledge my existence.

Samara paused outside the gate of Simon's courtyard. She closed her eyes and drew back images of the Nazarene. She saw the faces of the people in the front of the crowd, listening to him so attentively. He had looked at each of them as he spoke. She opened her eyes, straightened her back, and proceeded toward the house with a satchel of ointments tucked under her arm.

Once at the door, she lifted her hand to knock but stopped. She heard voices inside. Someone walked past the door, and it creaked open. The latch hadn't caught. Samara leaned forward to listen. Two men were talking in low voices.

"Simon, I see you have been preoccupied." It was the teacher's voice.

"You are attentive, aren't you? Now that we are alone, do you wish to try to win me over the way you have my guests?" There was the sound of someone standing up. Samara pushed the door open a little more and put her eye to the crack. Simon was standing, speaking accusingly to the teacher, who only looked back with peace. He seemed almost amused at the man's unrest.

"Yes, you come into my home and expect me to suddenly treat you as master of the house? Who is the guest here?" Jesus' face turned serious. He asked Simon to sit down and explain how he had offended him. Simon slammed his fist into his open palm.

"Why is it that every time you look at me, I see her?" He came closer and knelt down before Jesus. "Why does my past come back to haunt me after so many years?" These last words were lower, pleading. Jesus was looking him full in the face, listening with concern. Simon continued, now looking down to the ground. "I thought it would be best. I was terrified of becoming a father. You know, I never was looking for any commitment, and so I took off. I thought it would be best for her."

"Or did you think it would be best for you?"

Samara winced as Simon's head snapped up. "And now you judge my intention?" He stood up. "Why am I telling you this, anyway?" Again, he seemed more to be pleading than accusing. "Whose sin was it? Mine or hers?" The Nazarene nodded as the rest of the guests came back into the room. They paused at the table, looking from the preacher to Simon, wondering at their silence and the way they were looking at one another. Samara was about to pull her head back out when Jesus looked straight at her. She gasped and ducked back behind the door.

Mine, her mind cried. *It was my fault. I am the one with sin, and I am the one in need of forgiveness.* The truth exploded within her, and the tears she had held in check for so many years at last found their vent. All the loneliness and remorse welled up and poured over in a surge of emotion. *I have to see him now!* Forgetting about Simon, Samara pushed the door open and began to crawl into the room. She couldn't stand; she was aware of approaching someone holy, and she felt like a worm.

The room was dimly lit. One lonely lantern hung over the table at which the men were reclined. Jesus was still seated, his feet stretched to the side. He was listening intently to the other men, seeing and hearing only them. Simon sat at the table as well but was silently brooding. Every now and then he would glance at the preacher but was unable to catch his eye.

I want to finish our conversation. What did his nod mean? the

115

thoughts clouded his head and distracted him from noticing that Samara was creeping forward, moving across the wooden planks toward his guest. The men's voices grew louder at one point and she froze. She still hadn't been noticed. Coming up to the Nazarene, she pulled out her alabaster jar and, carefully breaking the neck off, poured its content over his feet. Instantly, the fragrance filled the room. Simon turned up his nose and breathed deeply. The man to his right noticed the woman. He was so shocked, all he could do was point and stare.

Never in their lives had those men seen such a spectacle. A woman, obviously wealthy, was bending over this prophet's feet, weeping, rubbing oils and wiping them with her long black hair. Jesus just watched her. When she had finished wiping his feet with her hair, she began to kiss them. As she pulled her hair back, Simon froze. *What is* she *doing here?* He turned, caught between trying to escape and calling a servant to throw her out. *Of all times and places,* now *she has to come.*

Just when he lifted his head to call a servant, he caught the eyes of the Nazarene. It occurred to him that if this man were a prophet, he would know who she was. Simon clenched his fists, fuming over the position he was unwillingly being put in. At the same time, he was terrified that Jesus did know and was waiting for the right time to humiliate them both. The prophet had been watching Simon and then spoke. "Simon, I have something to say to you."

Simon sank where he sat, not daring to look at him. "Tell me, teacher."

Jesus began, "Two people were in debt to a certain creditor." Simon looked up confusedly. "A parable?" Jesus seemed not to notice his confusion and continued. "One of the men owed five hundred days' wages and the other owed fifty. Since they were unable to repay the debt, he forgave them both. Which of them will love him more?"

Simon sat with his mouth open in confusion. *What was he getting at?* Simon hesitated, wondering where it was leading to, then stated, "Well, I suppose it would be the one whose larger debt was forgiven."

Jesus nodded. "You have judged rightly."

Simon continued to stare, still uncertain of what to do when Jesus spoke again. "Do you see this woman?"

Simon's cringed inside but nodded.

"When I entered your house, you did not give me water for my feet, but she has bathed them with her tears and wiped them with her hair. You did not give me a kiss, but she has not ceased kissing my feet since the time she entered. You did not anoint my head with oil, but she anointed my feet with ointment. So I tell you, her many sins have been forgiven; hence she has shown great love. But the one to whom little is forgiven loves little."

"Little is forgiven?" Simon whispered the words to himself, searching Jesus' gaze. "I am to blame." After six years, the truth broke through the barriers he had built up. Simon stared from Jesus back to Samara, who was still bent over. She hadn't looked at him. She hadn't noticed the dialogue taking place above her head. She was absorbed in obtaining forgiveness. "Forgiveness for our sin," thought Simon. He felt the Nazarene staring at him, waiting. Avoiding his gaze, Simon shook his head and sat back down. "I can't. Not yet… I just need space to think."

☙

Samara was now looking up toward Jesus. Pulling his gaze from Simon, he looked and said to her, "Samara, your sins are forgiven." Standing up, he helped her to her feet. "Your faith has saved you; go in peace." Simon watched as she broke into a fresh fit of weeping. They no longer were desperate cries, though. She stood up and her face was radiant. Jesus nodded his head to dismiss her, and she left.

"Where is she going?" Simon asked. "Is that all there is to it?"

Jesus turned to his host. "She is going to share with others the forgiveness she has received." Jesus waited a moment, but Simon still stood in the middle of the room, trying to work things out in his mind. "That's all? That's all." He looked to the preacher. "That's all." Jesus nodded respectfully.

"Very well, then. You know where to find me if ever…" Simon was walking to the door. He opened it, waiting for the preacher to leave. What he desperately wanted was a moment of silence to himself. The preacher thanked Simon and left. However, instead of closing the door behind him, Simon stayed to watch him walk away. In fact, he followed him out to the gate. The preacher stopped as he was about to leave the courtyard. He turned once more to Simon and smiled. "Perhaps we will meet again."

Simon found himself nodding. He looked down at his feet, and when he glanced up again, Jesus was walking down the road. Rain was beginning to drizzle. Simon tilted his head back to look straight into the falling drops of water. *Perhaps,* he thought. *Perhaps we will.*

The Hemorrhage Woman

"The souls of the just are in the hand of God, and no torment shall touch them. For if before men, indeed, they be punished, yet is their hope full of immortality. Chastised a little, they shall be greatly blessed, because God tried them and found them worthy of himself."

WISDOM 3:1, 4-5

Jairus watched as his wife sat weeping over their daughter. His little girl's breathing came out in short, rasping breaths. Her thin chest rose and fell with each gasp. He heard his brother quietly enter the room. Without taking his eyes off his daughter, he said in a trancelike voice, "It is going to kill me if she dies." His brother remained silent, unable to reach him in his suffering. Jairus' thoughts continued after his voice fell short. *She is only twelve. But what more can I do?* He closed his eyes and recalled the procession of doctors that had come. One after the other, they all left the same: heads shaking, giving complicated prognoses, and mumbling about the rarity of her case. There was nothing they could do. Jairus lifted his hand to massage his forehead. From under his hand he looked down at the hard-packed earthen floor. Loose dirt and bits of trash were scattered about. He looked up at the wall in front of him. A flimsy cloth covered the only window in the room. It was dirty from neglect, and the four walls closed around its inhabitants like the walls of a coffin. His chest tightened from the suffocating sorrow that closed around his heart.

He stood up and kissed his wife and daughter, leaving for another day at the synagogue. How he could work when his daughter was dying, he didn't know, but somehow he managed to drag himself through the routine motions of each day in order to run back to her bedside every night. And every night, his anticipation at seeing her was met with yet more despair. He couldn't take his mind off of her. He agonized throughout the day, wondering how she was, if she had died. Every person that came into the meeting room made his stomach flip. He always thought they were coming for him – to tell him she had gone. Every day, he imagined it eight different ways and as many different times. He stood in the council session that day with the other officials, half listening to their discussion and half thinking of his daughter, when something caught his attention.

"This healer is causing too much commotion."

"But Resheg, if he is ridding our streets of unclean people, curing their illnesses, and expelling demons, what do we care whose name he does it in, so long as he is cleaning our streets?"

"What do we care? We care a great deal," said another official with a long shaggy beard. "He is causing frenzy among the people."

Resheg insisted, "It's a frenzy that brings them to the synagogue and increases their fervor for the Law and the Sabbath. It is religious renewal."

"Healer or not, we have to be careful of false messiahs… Jairus, what do you say?"

The officials turned to him, and he only asked, "What healings does he do?"

A shorter, younger official rattled off from a scroll, "Giving sight to two blind men, restoring a withered hand, raising a young man from the dead in Nain… although that one is being investigated because it is thought to have been a hoax. He also is reported to have expelled demons in seven people and heal a man who had been badly burned in a house fire."

A ray of hope broke through the clouds of Jairus' heart as he listened. *Maybe he could heal my daughter,* he thought.

"Jairus, what do you say?" the elderly official asked again, waving his hand in front of his eyes. "Are you feeling alright? We need to make a statement about this man Jesus because he is in the area now. We need to say something about him before he leaves or the people will be carried away."

Jairus focused on him and asked, "Where is he?"

Resheg answered, "He usually goes down to the shore to preach. It is better for the crowds to hear him there." Jairus nodded and turned to leave. The three officials stared dumbly at one another and at his retreating figure. "He mustn't be feeling well," one of them said. They shrugged their shoulders and broke up the committee until their head should return.

෮෫

"I'm sorry, Helen, but there's nothing more we can do. It has been twelve years. You have been coming to me for the past six months, and each time it has been the same." The doctor paused as he measured Helen's expression. She was staring out the window at nothing. He continued, "Do you have any family? I suggest you spend time with them." His words faded as Helen began shaking her head.

"No, I have no family." She whispered more to herself than

to him. Shaking her head to clear her thoughts, she looked up. "Don't worry, though. You've done everything you can. I will take care of myself now. Maybe I'll go down to the sea… That will be a nice place to die. It's peaceful." Helen laughed to herself as she got up to leave. "At least I don't have to worry about leaving my wealth with anyone. I've spent everything on doctors. I don't have to worry about that now, though…" The doctor only sighed as Helen let herself out of his house. This job could be tough at times, but what more could he do? He went back to his desk to finish mixing a drug for another patient.

Jairus wove through the crowd of people standing and sitting at the lakeshore. A baby cried in the distance and two children ran in front of him, one stepping on his foot. Jairus didn't notice as the boy skittered off. Jairus was looking ahead, listening to the man preaching to this vast crowd. Standing on an overturned boat, the Nazarene addressed the crowd, not ranting and raving as some preachers did. He didn't even gesture or use elevated vocabulary or different languages. Rather, he spoke simply, clearly. Every now and then, he would point to the sky. His deep voice resonated across the water. Even with such a large crowd, everyone could hear. Jairus watched as he looked at the people he was speaking to. His eyes wouldn't roam the crowds but would stop on individuals – and yet somehow include everyone. Caught in admiration, Jairus' hands hung at his sides as he stood in silence. For a brief moment, he forgot why he had come as he simply observed.

After Jesus had finished, a group of men surrounded him. Jairus recognized them as some of John's followers. Having heard that they were following Jesus, it was obvious to note their esteem for this man of God. They listened to his every word. Jesus was answering them, but Jairus forgot about listening. The thought of his daughter came slamming through his mind, causing his heart to skip a beat. *What if she were already dead?* A wave of panic swept through him, crashing against his heart. Breaking through John's disciples, he interrupted Jesus. "My daughter is dying! Come and lay your hand on her so she may live!" The words spilled out before he could think of the scene he was creating. The crowd surrounding them fell silent. Time froze as Jesus waited in silence, his gaze boring into Jairus. He looked back desperately. He felt his heart plead, "You are my last hope." When Jairus felt he could take it no longer and was about to shout in anguish for him to save his daughter, Jesus nodded. Without a word, Jairus led the way with Jesus at his side. The crowd parted as the two silent men passed through them. A trail of followers proceeded, hoping to see a miracle that day.

Helen was standing just behind one of the Nazarene's disciples. She had come to the lake to die and had wound up listening to this man who sounded like a prophet. Something about him was curious to her and she had made her way in closer to get a better look. That was when Jairus had come up to speak to him. Helen had heard the entire exchange. She felt a surge of desperation as she saw that Jesus was actually going with Jairus. *Is he really a healer? Why else would he follow that official if he weren't?* Pushing herself up, she followed the group as they made their way to the town.

Long years of solitude were all Helen had stored in her memory. Shunned from even begging on the corner, she had grown used to being an outcast because of her illness. She trembled inside at being near so many people. If any of them knew she was unclean, she could be stoned. Shuddering at the thought, she nevertheless couldn't turn back now. She had come this far and was at the end of her rope. She had to continue on.

"If only I can get in close enough to touch the tassel of his cloak, I will be healed," Helen mumbled to herself, hoping and believing in this man of God. She had seen the way he looked at Jairus. The official hadn't noticed but the Nazarene's gaze was full of concern. This man had to be more than just a prophet if he were following a pleading synagogue official. Holding her breath and clutching at the last ray of hope in her fading body, Helen bent over and crawled. *Yes, just a tassel. That is enough to heal me.* Jesus had stopped to help a man who was being trampled by the crushing crowd. Reaching forward, Helen stretched out her arm to touch him.

All sound and movement seemed to fade as Helen brushed his cloak with her fingertips. It was a brief, almost imperceptible, contact, but she immediately felt her pain leave. It vanished with the wound.

Just as when a person lies down when ill with a fever and then wakes up after hours of sleep to find that he feels well again, a similar sensation coursed through Helen's veins. She sat on the ground as the crowd surged around above her. She sat there and felt her strength replenished with each breath of dusty air she breathed in. Looking down at herself, she examined her hands and arms and legs. *Unbelievable!* Joy erupted in her heart. *It was only his tassel, and that was enough. I am well!*

Moments before, Helen had been days away from death; now she couldn't get past her own astonishment. She was healed. She stood up straight only to find that Jesus had frozen before her. She also froze at the words he spoke to his disciples. "Who touched me?" He hadn't looked at her – in fact his back was to her – but she saw the impatience on his disciple's face as he answered, "Lord, you see how the crowd pushes in around you and yet you ask who touched you?" Helen sank back down to the ground.

Jairus had been leading but stopped when Jesus turned to ask who had touched him. His thoughts were flaring with impatience. *What is he doing now? My daughter is dying! Why does he care if someone touched him?*

Jesus didn't answer his disciple but spoke as if to himself in a whisper, "I know someone has touched me; I felt the power go from me." Helen caught the words and shrank inside. As she cowered on the ground, she saw the Nazarene begin to look about from face to face in the crowd.

Jairus moved up next to Jesus, ready to interrupt him. Thoughts of his daughter pressed the urgency closer and closer around his throat.

Helen whimpered to herself, "What if he finds out? What shame!" She closed her eyes in agony and the image of the look of concern Jesus had directed to Jairus came to her. She opened her eyes to see that Jesus had moved away from where she sat and was still searching for the one who had touched him. She swallowed hard and stood up. She had to confess her insincerity. From a few paces away, between the people, Jesus' search stopped on her. He stood there, waiting for her to speak.

Jairus watched Jesus' gaze fall upon a decrepit trembling woman. Helen stepped forward. She knelt down before him but didn't touch him. Instead, she began to weep as she explained, "Lord, I have been ill with a hemorrhage for twelve years." The crowd pulled away in disgust and indignation. Jairus instinctively took a step back with the rest of the disciples who were close to her. The woman on the ground was visibly shaking with shame. Jairus only thought of his daughter. *This is a waste of time! My daughter... my little girl.* He looked impatiently at the healer. Jesus was listening to the woman. Jairus scoffed at the sight.

With her face in her hands, her story came out in halting words. "I have spent my whole livelihood on doctor after doctor. Each answer has been the same. I was doomed to death. This very day I was told I had but days to live. I have no family, so I decided to go to the lake to die peacefully there. That is when I heard you speak."

At this she stopped and looked up at Jesus. He showed no sign of encouragement but neither any regret, so she continued, "I followed after you because I knew that if I could but touch the tassel of your cloak, I could be made well. So when you stopped, I reached forward, and immediately my wound dried up. I am healed! Lord please, have mercy on me." She buried her face in her hands, afraid to see what his answer would be.

The man who had healed her said, "Daughter." He then turned to Jairus, who had heard each word the woman had uttered. "Your faith has made you well. Go in peace."

Your faith… the words resounded in Jairus' mind. He couldn't take his eyes off the woman… twelve years… so many doctors… the same answer… Jairus recognized those words with painful familiarity. No longer scoffing, he looked at Jesus, confused. *Will he heal my girl as he healed this woman?* he thought. *Faith healed her, but can my faith heal another?*

A shout and movement broke the moment. Two of Jairus' servants came crashing through the crowd. Oblivious to the drama that had just taken place, one of them blurted out, "Your daughter is dead; do not trouble the teacher any longer." Jairus felt his heart drop. He reached out in desperation when Jesus grabbed his shoulder. He looked directly at him, reading his despair. "Stop fearing; have faith, and she will be saved."

Jairus found himself nodding even though his head spun with dizzying thoughts. He felt he had just been pushed from the heights of a great cliff. With Jesus now leading, he pressed forward. All he could think of was getting to his house, blocking out all doubts. He began to push through the crowd, but just before leaving the square, he looked back to glance at the woman. She was standing alone now, watching the crowd depart. A surge of hope filled Jairus as he clung to faith in the man beside him. His daughter might still be healed.

As soon as they turned onto the street where his house was, Jairus could already hear the mourners wailing loudly. The light of hope vanished as his stomach clenched in agony. Jesus turned to the crowd that had followed and motioned for three of his disciples, telling the others to keep everyone away. When the five men approached the house, Jesus called out to the mourners in a commanding voice. "Do not weep so. She has not died but is only sleeping." The wailing turned immediately to laughter and Jairus really felt he was going to be ill. He pushed away the doubt these foul people had awakened in him. Stepping forward, he bellowed to them to leave his property immediately. Grumbling and pushing one another, they filed out his front gate. They ridiculed Jesus as they left, but he didn't pay attention. He walked past them into the house, where he dismissed all the servants and neighbors. Jairus could only watch as he took control. He had his three disciples get everyone out. After that he turned to Jairus. "Show her to me." Jairus pointed down the hall. He could hear his wife's muffled sobs.

Jesus' firmly set face softened at the weeping he heard. He moved forward. Jairus and the others followed. They entered the room quietly. His little girl's white face shone out from the dark blankets that covered her. She was so still. Jesus came to the bed and knelt beside it. He began to pray. He held one of the little white hands in between his. He bowed his head while his lips moved in silent petition. Jairus stood in the corner of the room. He was afraid to hope and yet longed to believe. He closed his eyes to keep from crying, and from behind the darkness he saw the face of the woman in town. He saw her confidence and heard the voice of the one who healed her. Holding his breath and clutching on to one last ray of hope, Jairus bowed his head and began to pray as well. After a few minutes, Jesus leaned forward and whispered, "Child, arise!"

Jairus looked up to hear her gasp, as if she were coming up from under water. She coughed. Her face flooded with color, and she opened her eyes. The three disciples looked from one another with uncertainty. Jairus took a step back, almost fearing what he saw. But his little girl simply looked about at the strange and shocked faces before her. Once she spotted her mother she sprang up and ran to her. Jairus' wife had been in silent astonishment until her child reached her. She again dissolved into tears, this time of joy. Jairus stood frozen, unable to believe his eyes. The little girl before him, happy and smiling, must be a vision. The vision turned to him and smiled. He reached out and touched the miracle he had only hoped for. He picked his little girl up into his arms and held her close until Jesus interrupted. "Perhaps she should be given something to eat."

Jairus' wife almost fainted. "Food! Darling, you haven't eaten in three days!" Jairus yelled for a servant who had evaded the disciples and was lingering behind the door. After the servant left, Jairus looked at the Nazarene, who was watching him intently. Jairus fumbled through his mind, trying to look for words of gratitude. Jesus nodded in understanding and said, "Jairus, tell no one of this. It is not yet my time." Jesus reached over and patted his daughter on the head, then left with his disciples following.

"Papa!" Jairus turned to his daughter. "I had the strangest dream about a woman who was sick and helped heal you!"

Jairus sat down on the bedside. Finally, he said, "No, my daughter. It wasn't the woman, it was her faith."

The Samaritan Woman

"To the thirsty I will give a gift from the spring of life-giving water. The victor will inherit these gifts, and I shall be his God, and he will be my son."
REVELATION 21:6-7

The high noon sun scorched down on the empty streets of Sychar. A hot gust of wind sent tumbleweed flying through the square. The door of a lonely, dilapidated house creaked open enough for a slit of darkness to be seen. A woman peered out from the slit at the lonely afternoon. The next moment, the door swung back and the woman emerged. She was dressed in muddy-looking garb. The sandals she had on were worn through to the heel. One of them flapped every other step she took. That was the only noise to be heard. Under her arm, she carried a red clay jar. There was a crack in it that made it possible to bring home only half of what it could carry.

"Water, water. I need water," she mumbled to herself. "Get to the well… before anyone sees. I need some water. It's been hot. Water, water." She hurried through the streets of Sychar with her head down. Her eyes darted back and forth, watching, troubled. At one point, her broken sandal caught on a plank of wood in the road. She tripped forward. Her jar spiraled across the dirt as she caught her fall with her hands. The dust enveloped her and she hacked a dry, harsh cough.

When she got up, she limped over to her jar, bent down painfully, and retrieved it. She looked up and saw a little boy emerging from an alley. He screamed in a high-pitched voice, "Ahhh! Witch! It's the witch!" He picked up a stone to throw at her. She reached out and grabbed his hand. Her bony fingers gripped his skinny arm and he howled in pain.

"Silence!" she sneered at him. "Be silent, little rat! I will curse you and your family if you don't stop!" He bit his lip to stop and stared at her through huge eyes brimming with tears and dread. The woman stopped seething at him and watched as one tear made a trail down his dirt-streaked face. He must have been only eight. She loosened her fingers, and he pulled his arm free. He didn't run away but stayed fixed where he stood, looking at her. He then jumped, remembering who she was, and bolted away. The woman stayed where she was. She still held her jar under one arm while the other hung limply at her side. She sighed at the spot where the boy had been. A dog barked in the house next to her. Startled, she snapped to and continued toward the well. "Water, water…"

❣

At last, the well came into sight. She kept her head down and quickened her pace. The well was located in the center of Sychar, a town in the north of Samaria. Their ancient father Jacob had made that well there for his sons and cattle to drink from. The people of Sychar prided themselves for such a significant ancestral relic. This, however, was not on the woman's mind as she approached it. Water was on her mind.

Reaching the well, she began pulling the rope to bring up

the bucket. The rope slid easily through the grooves that were worn into the edge of the well, grooves made from hundreds of years and even more hands that pulled at the rope for water. The well had never run dry. Generations of Samaritans had been sustained by its wealth. This, however, was not on the woman's mind – she was only thinking of water. So much so, that the man sitting in the shade of a nearby tree went unnoticed. He stood and approached the woman, whose head was down as she pulled at the rope. She gave a final tug and reached out to hull the bucket up. Her arms strained with effort.

The man watched, fascinated at how engrossed she was. He spoke. "Give me a drink." The woman shrieked and sent the bucket plummeting back down the dark hole. The rope zipped through the groove in the stone and would have perished with the bucket had the man not clamped his foot on the end that lay on the ground. He picked it up and wrapped it around the hook used to secure the rope.

The woman stared hard at him with critical eyes. When he had finished, he turned to her. She gasped and pointed at him with an accusing finger. "I see who you are! How dare you, a Jew, ask me, a woman and a Samaritan, for a drink?" With her finger still extended, she circled around him to where her jar lay by the well. He didn't take his eyes from her as she bent to pick it up. His eyes smiled at her, though his mouth didn't. She suddenly froze. There was something about his gaze that made her stop. She began to mumble, "No, no water for you. Jew. You're a Jew. Can't talk to Jews." But she stayed staring at him, much the same as she had with the boy.

The man lifted his eyebrows in question. She noticed his lips were parched and realized that his voice had seemed husky when he had spoken. His tunic was covered in dust, obviously the dust of a long travel. She looked back to his face. "No, no water," she continued mumbling as she lowered her head.

He took a step back and held out his hands. "If you knew the gift of God...." Her head snapped up and she fell silent. The man spoke again. "If you knew who was asking you, 'Give me a drink,' you would have asked him," he pointed to himself, "and he would have given you living water."

"Living water?" she whispered. She looked at the jar in her hands, then to his empty ones. "Sir," she stated, "you have no jar, and the well is deep. How do you expect to retrieve that living water?" A touch of sarcasm tinted her words. He didn't answer, so she pushed further. "Do you expect to be greater than our father Jacob, who gave us this well?" The man looked at the well the woman was pointing to.

He answered, "Everyone who drinks of this water will thirst again." Glancing at the woman, he went on. "Whoever drinks of the water that I give will never thirst." The woman frowned as he continued, "The water I give will become a spring of water welling up to eternal life."

"Eternal life," she whispered to herself again. Her gaze focused on a point beyond the man's shoulder. He turned to see what she was looking at but saw nothing. "Sir." He turned back to her, but she was still speaking to herself. "Never thirst again. I will never need water again." A light entered her eyes and she smiled. She focused on the man. Stepping forward, she fell to her knees, dropping the jar, and grabbed at the man's tunic. "Sir, give me this water that I may not thirst, nor come here to draw water ever again."

He didn't pull away, as she had expected him to. He only stayed there, with pity in his eyes. She suddenly realized what she had done. The woman jumped up and began to brush the dust from her dirty mantle. She kept her eyes lowered and shifted from one foot to the other. Taking a deep breath, she looked up to the man for an answer. His eyes bore into hers. She began to fidget.

"Go, call your husband and come here." The woman's mouth fell open and her eyes filled with shock and horror. She swallowed hard and forced the words, "I have no husband." One of her eyes started twitching.

He shook his head. "You are right," he said. "You have no husband." The woman tightened her jaw and clasped her hands behind her back. He continued, "Rather, you have had five husbands." She lowered her head. "And the one you are with now; he is not your husband." The woman looked up with anguish and began wringing her hands.

She paced back and forth in the dust. He stayed where he was. "I see," she began, "that you are a prophet." She lifted her hand and began to straighten her veil, smoothing its wrinkles in vain. She looked out at the mountain Sychar was nestled under. "You know, sir," she said, still tugging at her veil, "our fathers worshipped on this mountain; and you Jews say that Jerusalem is the place men ought to worship." She brought her arms up and crossed them in front of her.

Instead of becoming agitated, as she expected, the man answered in his same, calm voice, "Woman, believe me, the hour is coming when neither on this mountain nor in Jerusalem will you worship the Father." She raised her eyebrows in surprise. He continued, "You worship what you do not know; we worship what we know, for salvation is from the Jews." The woman's crossed arms fell to her side. She sighed deeply, staring at the well. "But the hour is coming," he stated. The man stepped toward her, and she looked at him as he spoke. "Indeed, the hour is now when the true worshipers will worship the Father in spirit and truth, for such the Father seeks them to worship him." She whispered, "Truth." The man nodded, saying, "God is spirit, and those who worship him must worship in spirit and truth." The woman nodded in return. She answered, "I know that the Messiah is coming; when he comes he will show us all things…" Her voice faded away into her own imaginings of the glorious coming. She looked at the man with helpless yearning. She shrugged her shoulders in defeat.

The man said, "I who speak to you am he. I am the Messiah." Her shoulders slumped and she took a step back. Down the street, a group of men could be heard approaching. She stood still, looking at him, her lips moving in silent words. The men approaching fell silent when they realized they were interrupting a conversation. They all looked to the man who had been conversing with the woman. He seemed not to notice they were there. He continued to look at the woman. Her head was down and she spoke softly to herself. After some moments, she looked up with radiant eyes. She nodded to the man and turned to leave, whispering, "The Messiah… spirit and truth." Her water jar lay on its side, forgotten on the ground. The wind blew and gently rocked it.

☙

One man from the group stepped forward with a loaf of bread. He said, "Rabbi, eat." The teacher looked at the man and shook his head. He walked over to the well and began pulling on the rope. "I have food to eat of which you do not know." One of the disciples in the group whispered to another, "Has someone brought him food?"

The man looked at them and said, "My food is to do the will of him who sent me and to accomplish his work." The disciples stared at him, trying to understand. He continued, "Do you not say, 'There are yet four months, then comes the harvest'? I tell you, lift up your eyes and see how the fields are already white for harvest. I am sending you to reap that for which you did not labor." He pulled the bucket up to the edge of the well. "Others have labored before you, and you have entered into their labor." The man took a cup sitting next to the well. He dipped it into the bucket of water, filling it. He raised it to his lips and drank deeply.

Mary Magdalene

"As a shepherd tends his flock when he finds himself among his scattered sheep, so will I tend my sheep. I will rescue them from every place where they were scattered when it was cloudy and dark... I myself will pasture my sheep; I myself will give them rest, says the Lord God. The lost I will seek out, the strayed I will bring back..., shepherding them rightly."

EZEKIEL 34:12,15-16

A limp body was dragged out of the ring of soldiers. A trail of deep red streaked the stones. The men marched out, and my Lord was out of sight. I couldn't breathe, I couldn't think. My mind was frozen in horror as the images of bear claws tearing at his flesh flashed before my eyes. In slow motion they returned; the gems of ruby soared through the air and christened the faces of those demonic guards who were flaying the man. Movement shattered the vision, and I saw Mary step into the middle of the arena. She lightly stepped around the puddles of red, looking at them sorrowfully, clutching white shrouds that Pilate's wife had hurriedly thrust into her hands. She got down on her hands and knees and carefully began to dab at his blood. There was something almost holy in the way she cleaned it. Many years have I witnessed the slaughter of sacred lambs for the Passover; the way she was gathering his blood is only comparable to the care with which the priests collected the lamb's blood, no drop touching the ground.

Mary's sweeping motions moved back and forth, their graceful movements a striking contrast to the lumbering brutality of the guards. What their slashing whips had spilt, her blessed hands were drawing back.

I walked over and stooped down to do the same. A tear rolled off my cheek and sent ripples into the puddle I was mopping at. A scene of muscled arms streaking down like lightening on his back burst into my head. Hooks and nails slashing his skin and the grunts and yells from the soldiers assaulted my senses. There was so much blood. *My Lord, how could you do this? Why didn't you ever stand up?* My heart cried out in agony. All I could see was his thrashed body looking more like a worm than the man who had saved me only the year before.

☙

Kicks and curses were all that registered. The rope around my waist jerked me forward, and I tripped. The gritty taste of dust and dirt was in my mouth and nose. It mingled with the blood from my cut lip. Voices argued with one another, though I didn't make the effort to distinguish what they were saying. The terror that clawed at my throat and tore at my stomach kept my mind from doing anything. I was going to die; I knew it. They wanted to stone me. Where then, were they taking me? I was pulled up and hauled into the middle of a group of men. I could see some of the Sanhedrin. Before I could get a good look at who was going to kill me, I was thrown to the ground and greeted by the same earthy taste of dirt and the smell of too many men, more like swine. Men were shouting. One shrill voice rang above the others, giving an order. Then a calmer one, speaking, not yelling, cut off all noise. I braced myself for the first stone. My back tensed, ready to take the blow. It seemed like an eternity, waiting there for them to unleash their fury. A new sound greeted my ears, though. There was murmuring. I heard a small thud some ways off. With my ear still to the ground, I heard scratching in the dust around me. It sounded like a stick being dragged along the ground. Another thud, and another. Each time I flinched as I reacted to the noise, expecting pain to accompany it but feeling nothing. Now the ground thundered with dull thumps, but still, I was untouched. Then feet shuffled away, one by one, and there was silence.

Slowly, cautiously, I moved the hair out of my face and saw sandals in front of me. I don't know how, but I knew it was the calm voice that had stopped my death. Terror seized me. Who was this man that had saved me? What would I be expected to do to repay him? I did the first thing that came to my mind. With painstaking caution, I reached out and touched his ankle. Pulling myself closer, I gently kissed his foot. Then – did I dare? Finding a boldness inside me, I raised my head to peer at this man. My eyes met a hand, extended, welcoming. Of its own accord, mine found refuge in his. I looked up into his eyes and peace flooded through me.

He was so serene, so confident; his gaze held so much. There was more in his eyes than a million scrolls can contain. No scribe could depict the depths of them, no king could measure their richness, and they were focused on me. He grasped my hand and pulled me to my feet. Taking his tunic to wipe the blood from my lip, he said, "What? Has no one condemned you?" I shook my head no. "Well, then, neither do I. Go, and sin no more." With that he turned and walked away. I was left alone in the now-empty square, but his presence filled every space in the street and in my heart. Who was that man?

⊗

A river of tears was now streaming down my face. I could not contain it any more as sobs racked my body. I sat back on my heels and arms surrounded me as Mary embraced me. "Shhh, my daughter," she whispered. "He will triumph. Don't lose hope." I looked into her face and through her own tears I encountered the same gaze that saved me when last it seemed all hope was lost. Her frame trembled with sorrow and suffering. I know that each tremor passing through her was another memory of what her Son had endured. "How can she console me? Her son is the one dying." We both froze as we heard feet pounding the pavement. Afraid of what was to come next, we looked up to see John come running over to us. "Mother! He's being judged now. Let us go." He said it compassionately, sensitive to her suffering. I rose on weak knees. With Mary between us to support her, we hastened to the praetorium.

Mary's Memory

"I will bless the Lord at all times; praise shall be always in my mouth. My soul glory in the Lord that the poor may hear and be glad."

PSALM 34:2-3

I found myself alone. I looked around at the walls of the room, the small window that showed a patch of blue sky, the mat rolled up in the corner, the little stand that held my prayer candle on it. One drop of wax was slowly making its way down the side of the candle. I watched it sink and then realized that the candle had gone out. It had blown out with the rush of wind that he left on.

"The angel... His words ran through my mind, sinking down to my heart. 'Do not be afraid, Mary... with God, nothing is impossible.' I looked around again. The room was still the same. I looked at my hands and felt my face and veil; everything was normal. But something was different. I stood and went out to where my mother was sweeping the floor. She didn't seem to have noticed.

"I turned back to my room and knelt down again. I waited. Maybe the angel would come back and tell me what to do next. After some time I stopped, thinking that even if he did, I couldn't wait forever. I stopped waiting for the angel and started praying to my God…"'I know it wasn't a dream. I believe you speak through the instruments you choose,' I said. The angel's words came back to me: "You have found favor with God… you will conceive in your womb and bear a son and you shall call him Jesus." The Messiah. 'You have chosen me to be the vessel of hope for your people,' I said. 'How long your people have prayed and waited for your coming. I have seen their plight. I have heard their pleas and wondered when the Chosen One would appear among us. And now the day is come: 'The Lord God will give to him the throne of his father David and he will reign over the house of Jacob forever…'

"As I prayed, I remembered all the times in my life when God had been there: all the gifts and graces he had given me. Who am I that he should have chosen me to bear the Messiah? He made me in my mother's womb. He gave me life by creating me. And yet, as his creature, he loved me. In this love, he chose me to love him in return. My heart swelled with gratitude and joy. Conscious of my poverty but certain of his grace, I knelt with my forehead pressed to the ground and kissed the loving hand that was reaching out to me, accepting the gift he was giving.

"My wonder was so great that I couldn't help but ask, how? I was a young girl, betrothed to Joseph but promised to virginity for the Lord. 'The Holy Spirit will come upon you and the power of the Most High will overshadow you; the child to be born will be called the Son of God.'

"I didn't ask for it. I wasn't seeking to be the chosen woman. God created me because he wanted it. I was made for this purpose. I looked up and saw the goodness of the one offering me this sublime gift. There was no hesitation. 'Let it be done to me according to his will,' I responded. He created me. I am his hand-maiden. I bowed my head before God's plan, and, when I lifted it again, the angel had departed.'"

☙

"Then what did you do?"

The veiled woman looked up at the young man before her. "Luke, Peter was so gracious to send you here to me. How can I thank you?" Luke had been holding her hand to help her sit down on the side of the sloping hill they had slowly been climbing. He pulled that hand toward him and kissed it.

"Mother, I am the one who is grateful." He smiled and sat down beside her. "But what did you do after the angel left?"

She was dressed in black and gray, and her bright brown eyes, almost honey in color, shone out from under the dark veil. Graying wisps of once-black hair escaped the confines of the veil and rustled gently in the breeze. Mary didn't notice her hair. She was gazing at the water, watching the sunlight play off of the rippling surface. Luke watched her as she sat there, lost in thought. She smiled to herself and turned her attention back to Luke.

"The angel had told me my cousin Elizabeth was with child. 'Your kinswoman Elizabeth in her old age has also conceived a son, and this is the sixth month with her who was called barren,' he said. I sat in my room praying after he left. I don't know how long I was there. Mother came in at one point to make sure I wasn't ill and then again to call me for supper... The angel's words kept running through my mind. The entire exchange with him sank deeper into my heart as I pondered them. As I went to supper with my parents, I was unable to converse much – I was too lost in thought and prayer – until I remembered what he had said about cousin Elizabeth. She was very much advanced in years. If it is difficult enough for a young mother to give birth to her first-born, I imagined Elizabeth would need more help.

ॐ

"'Miriam, did you hear what I said?' I looked up at my mother.

"'I'm sorry, I was lost in thought.'

Mother eyed me curiously, then said, 'Your cousin Elizabeth is expecting. Your father just received word from Zechariah today. An angel appeared to him when he was serving in the Temple. Zechariah didn't believe the angel's message that he was to be a father, so the angel struck him dumb. And now, Elizabeth is about to give birth…'

"I listened attentively to the story, my heart beating faster and faster. It was as though my mother were confirming all that had just happened only a few hours earlier. I stared into space, again lost in thought.

"'Miriam, are you sure you are feeling well? You are all flushed and distracted.' Mother came over to feel my forehead. I looked up at her with tears in my eyes.

"'Mother, may I go attend to Elizabeth?'"

ॐ

Mary stopped suddenly and stared out at the water with a slight smile on her face. Luke waited a few minutes, then pressed on.

"I remember you telling me about Elizabeth and how the Spirit was with her and John, even while he was still in the womb, but how did you tell everyone else that you were expecting the Messiah?"

She turned her gaze from the water to Luke as if to explain but instead sighed quietly.

"Mother, if you are tired, we can return now and you can continue later."

She reached over and patted his arm. "You are very thoughtful. Perhaps I can continue later."

When she didn't stand to go, Luke ventured one more question.

"Were you afraid?"

Mary looked up with surprise and answered immediately. "Why should we fear when God is in control? You know he could never do anything to harm us but has only shown us love." She paused and then went on, almost to herself. "No. There were many emotions within me but there was never any fear. I knew that I must give myself completely to God's plan, so in my heart, I trusted." Looking back to Luke she continued, "He has never abandoned us!"

Silence ensued. A bird soared above them, swooping down toward the water to land on the decks of one of the fishing boats that was bobbing lazily.

Luke watched, leaning back on his elbow on the grassy hillside. The bird left its perch and flew out of sight. Luke sat up straight and turned to face Mary.

"I am so grateful that you are here to share all these things; especially for those of us who never met him."

Mary looked into his honest, eager eyes. "Perhaps you never met him, but he knows you very well, Luke. Remember, 'Before I formed you in the womb, I knew you.'"

Luke nodded and said, "Spending time with you helps me know him better. I can almost hear his voice and see him blessing me, forgiving me, strengthening me…" His voice trailed off and Mary patted his arm again.

"He left us, but he's still here, Luke. I'll leave someday, but he will remain, continuing to bless, forgive, and strengthen."

The two sat in silence as the sun made its steady decline through the sky, slowly sinking behind the hills across the sea. As it sank, a slight breeze picked up to chill the air. Luke stood and held out his hand to Mary. She smiled at him and took his hand as he helped her up. Taking her arm in his, they started their way down the hill. They walked on together in silence, treasuring all their memories, reflecting on them in their hearts.

Per Regnum Christi ad Gloriam Dei